Study Guide for

Health

and

Social Care

Support Workers

2nd edition

NVQ / SVQ
In Care

10
Step-By-Step
Modules

Beverly Robertson

and

Stephen O'Kell

Acknowledgments

Sincere thanks and appreciation to the countless care professionals who contributed technical assistance.

Special thanks to: **Les Storey**, RGN, MITD, CMS, FETC, Vocational Development Manager, Lancashire College of Nursing and Health Studies, Lancashire

Kate Corkery Spencer, Editorial Assistant

Tom Bowman, Illustrator

First Class Books
P.O. Box1, Portishead,
Bristol BS20 9BR
Telephone: (0823) 323 126
Fax: (0823) 321 876

Introduction

Scottish and National Vocational Qualifications (S/NVQs) in Care provide a set of performance standards for health care support workers, nursing assistants, care assistants, and miscellaneous carers. The care standards specify the quality of performance in the workplace for people who deliver hands-on care. Achieving the standards also develops competence for assisting care professionals in institutional and non-institutional settings.

S/NVQs have been developed on a core plus endorsement model. The core highlights skills and knowledge that are needed by all care staff, regardless of the care setting or client group. This study guide provides the enabling knowledge relating to the six core units of the Level 2 awards:

- promoting equality for all individuals

- contributing to the ongoing support of the people in care and others who are significant to them

- supporting people in transition due to their care requirements

- contributing to the health, safety, and security of individuals and their environment

- obtaining, transmitting, and storing information relating to the delivery of care service

- contributing to the protection of individuals from abuse

The endorsement part of an S/NVQ is a particular selection of relevant work skills and knowledge that match a range of identified care roles with the occupational sector. This guide provides some of enabling knowledge relating to the following Level 2 S/NVQ in Care endorsements:

- developmental care
- direct care
- domiciliary support
- independent living support
- activity and access support
- residential/hospital support
- special care needs
- post-natal care
- combined support

Contents

Module 1

The Health Care Support Worker and Social Care Assistant

You are an important member of the care team.

Objectives:

- ☐ Identify duties and concerns
- ☐ Discuss the importance of the care team
- ☐ Explain the rights of people receiving care
- ☐ Identify legal issues
- ☐ Demonstrate respect for others' beliefs

Need-to-know Words:
- confidentiality
- work role
- respect and dignity
- care team
- rights
- beliefs
- equality
- abuse

Part 1	**Being Professional** *(O.b)*

Always be dependable.

Always treat people the way you would like to be treated if you were the one needing assistance. Know the limits and boundaries of your work role.

Earn people's trust and respect by acting in a professional way. Set high standards for yourself, and follow the established requirements and procedures.

Your attitude and actions affect how people feel about you. Your behaviour also affects how people in your care feel about themselves. Everything about you sends signals and affects how people react to you; e.g., the way you stand or move, your appearance, the way you dress, facial expressions, gestures, the tone of your voice.

Confidentiality

Information about the people in your care is very private. Confidential information includes all medical information (diagnosis, prognosis, and treatment) and everything related to personal, social, and financial matters.

You have both a legal and moral responsibility to keep the information confidential. Information is disclosed only to those who have the right or need to know according to statutory and agency policies. Never disclose information unless you have proof of the enquirer's identity and right of access.

There may be times when you learn that someone is at risk. Carefully explain to the person who told you that you may have to share the information with others.

All records with confidential information should be kept secure when not in use and should never be discussed in public. If you suspect abuse of confidential information, or if you have any concerns about confidentiality, seek advice from an appropriate person.

Dedication and Loyalty

Be dedicated to the people in your care. Remember that no task is unimportant if it contributes to a person's well-being. Provide ongoing support for people in your care and those who are significant to them.

Being a care provider requires you to take good care of yourself physically and emotionally so that you can bring health and happiness into the workplace. Keep yourself neat and clean, and demonstrate a caring attitude.

Be loyal to your employer. Support the objectives of the organisation by contributing to the health, safety, and security of people in your care and their environment.

Honesty and Integrity

Always maintain the security of the building and people's personal belongings. There may be legal action if possessions are lost.

Perform duties to the best of your ability. If in doubt, request clear instructions. Know and follow the employer's work rules and follow the Patient's Charter (see page 8).

Reliability

The people in your care and other staff members must be able to depend on you. Be on time for work, well-groomed, and in proper uniform (if required). If you are unable to work, notify your manager at the earliest opportunity.

Observe and chart information accurately. Notify your manager promptly of any significant physical, social, or psychological problems pertaining to the people in your care.

Respect

Promote and support equality for each individual. Always show respect for the people in your care, their families, and staff members (even if you dislike them).

Unacceptable Behaviours

The following are unacceptable behaviours:

· using verbal or physical abuse

· stealing or willfully damaging property

· disobeying an order from your manager

· neglecting your duties

· altering or falsifying any records or reports

· working under the influence of alcohol or drugs

· lying

Part 2	Working as a Team

The care team is concerned with the well-being of each person in their care.

The care team looks after the total well-being of each person in their care. The person receiving care is the most important member of the team. You are also an important member of that team. You are likely to spend more time with the people in your care than the other members of the team. Your attitude and skills have a significant effect on the quality of care provided.

People who are receiving care should have a say in the care services that are provided for them. They should be encouraged to be as self-managing as possible.

As a team member, you need to understand your organisation's administrative structure, policies, procedures, and reporting mechanisms. Support workers are under the direct supervision of professionals. Your work is under the supervision, direction, or guidance of professional staff accountable in the relevant area of practice.

The care team includes everyone with responsibility for care:

· doctors

· social workers

· dietitians

· nurses

· voluntary workers

· psychologists

· midwives

· therapists

· relatives/advocates

· health visitors

Care Plans

The care team develops an individual care plan for each person in their care. The plan outlines present and future care needs and ways these will be met.

Carrying out assessments and care plans, and evaluating the results should be a team effort. Get to know the care plan for each person, and follow the instructions carefully for providing care.

Total care includes everything that contributes to a person's well-being:

· balanced diet

· appropriate medical and clinical attention

· exercise and rest

· relationships and social activities

· financial security

Part 3	**Respecting People's Rights** *(O.a.b.c.d.e)*

Promote and support individual rights and choices.

Promote and support the rights of each person in your care, and encourage them to express their needs and wishes. Provide quality care regardless of the person's beliefs, gender, mental or physical ability, background, race, or sexuality. Your personal beliefs and preferences should not affect the quality of service.

Caring for People in the Community *(U1,W2.d)*

Provisions were established by the Department of Health in 1990 for Local Authorities to be responsible for planning the provision of community care services in their localities in conjunction with:

· District Health Authorities

· Family Health Service Authorities

· Local Housing Authorities

· Voluntary Organisations

These provisions were established for people who need care in the community:

· domiciliary, day, and respite services to enable people to live in their own homes, wherever feasible and sensible

· a full assessment of needs and the delivery of a negotiated package of services to meet those needs

· practical support for families who provide care for relatives at home

The Patient's Charter *(O, U5.c, W8.b)*

The Patient's Charter was established by the Department of Health in 1991. The document clearly sets out people's right to care and standards of service. The charter has seven existing rights, three new rights, and nine standards.

Existing Rights:

· to receive health care on the basis of clinical need, regardless of the ability to pay

· to be registered with a general practitioner

· to receive emergency medical care at any time

· to be referred to a consultant who is personally acceptable and to be referred for a second opinion

- to be given clear explanations of any proposed treatment, including any risks and alternatives, before agreeing to the treatment

- to have access to a person's own health records and the contents kept confidential

- to choose whether or not to take part in medical research or medical student training

New Rights:

- to be provided with detailed information on local health services, including quality standards and maximum waiting times

- to be guaranteed admission for treatment by a specific date, no later than two years from the date the person was placed on the waiting list

- to have any complaint that a person may have about the National Health Service (NHS) investigated and to receive a prompt and full written reply to the complaint

Standards:

- respect for privacy, dignity, and religious and cultural beliefs

- arrangements to ensure everyone can use the services, including people with special needs

- provision of information to relatives and friends

- ambulance service arriving at an emergency within 14-19 minutes

- immediate assessment in the Accident and Emergency Department

- being seen within 30 minutes of appointment time in the Outpatient Clinic

- operations not being cancelled on the day of operation

- a named nurse or midwife responsible for each patient

- arrangements made before discharge from hospital to ensure appropriate care is provided at home

Part 4	**Respecting People's Beliefs** *(O.d)*

Recognise and support individual beliefs and preferences.

Actively encourage people in your care to express their beliefs, wishes, and views, as long as they do not interfere with the rights of others. Personal beliefs and preferences are important. Acknowledge individual beliefs about self, religion, politics, culture, ethics, and sexuality. Respond in a manner that is supportive.

Beliefs and preferences affect the foods people eat, the clothing they wear, how they worship, and other practices of daily living. You can support individual beliefs in a variety of ways:

- Be sensitive to each person's needs.

- Support the right to practice individual beliefs.

- Make sure your speech and actions do not offend others.

- Address individuals in their preferred manner (title, name, nickname).

- Consider beliefs and lifestyles when taking part in care planning.

- Be respectful of each person's customs and possessions.

- Show interest in each person's beliefs.

- Be willing to listen when a person wants to talk.

- Never question or make fun of another's beliefs.

- Never try to force your religious beliefs on another person.

Learn all you can about religions, customs, and beliefs, including practices of ethnic minorities in your local area. Ask people to tell you about their beliefs and traditions, or go to the local library for information.

Religious Customs

Be familiar with religious customs. The more you know, the less likely you are to accidently offend someone. People may have religious items in their rooms (such as rosaries or prayer books). If you must move these items, handle them with respect.

Holidays

Be aware of days that are celebrated with special rituals. People may need extra help dressing for holidays or they may need privacy for certain rituals (such as confession or prayer).

Foods

Some religions forbid certain foods. Know what is not allowed and offer other choices. Be aware of special times that people may fast (go without food) or eat only certain foods.

Clothing

Some religions have certain articles of clothing that should be treated with respect.

Medical Treatments

Be aware of any medical treatments that are not allowed because of religious beliefs.

Clergy

If a person wants to see a clergy member, make sure your manager is informed. Provide privacy whenever a clergy member visits.

| Part 5 | Promoting Equality (O.a) |

Everyone deserves to be treated with respect and dignity.

Your personal beliefs affect your behaviour in a variety of direct and indirect ways. Never allow your beliefs to interfere with the quality of service for anyone in your care. National guidelines and local organisational policies prohibit discriminatory practices (unfair treatment).

To promote equality, it is important to recognise and accept other people's beliefs and lifestyles (even if they clash with your own). Every individual has the right to equality and quality of life, regardless of age, gender, physical or mental ability, race, culture, religion, or other factors affecting discrimination. Seek advice if you are unsure of appropriate behaviour or if you have discriminatory feelings.

Protect yourself and others from discrimination by taking appropriate action:

· Carefully examine any feelings of hostility.

· Provide feedback to anyone who has been discriminatory about the effects and consequences of his or her actions.

· Offer support and guidance to people who have been discriminated against and to those at risk from discrimination.

· Make a formal complaint about any discrimination, or support others in doing so.

Part 6 — Protecting Individuals from Abuse *(U5, Z1.a.c)*

Report all complaints and any suspected abuse.

It is your legal responsibility to respect people's rights and to protect them from physical or mental harm. Legal action may result from abuse or failure to report suspected abuse. If a person in your care has a complaint, report it.

Protect people from any physical or mental harm:

abuse	mental, physical, sexual, medical, or financial abuse, exploitation, or neglect
assault	an unlawful personal attack
battery	an attack where an actual blow is delivered
defamation	falsehoods that result in damage to a person's reputation or character
	libel: a written statement slander: a spoken statement
false documentation	entries in a person's record that are not true or have been altered
negligence	failure to give assigned care, or giving improper care that causes harm
	(e.g., failure to raise bedrails, leading to someone falling from the bed)

If a person in your care needs protection from abuse, be sure that you know the care plan and any rules or regulations that pertain to the situation.

Help minimise the risk of abuse by offering advice and support, as appropriate, to help people understand why their inappropriate behaviour may be seen as abusive.

If you suspect abuse, report your evidence immediately to the person-in-charge, and make a detailed written record.

If you have any concerns about dealing with abuse in the work environment, seek advice from an appropriate person.

Review

1. Why is confidentiality important?

_____

_____

_____

_____

2. Identify unacceptable behaviours.

_____

_____

_____

_____

3. What is the role of the care team?

_____

_____

_____

_____

4. What is a care plan?

_____

_____

_____

_____

5. What is the purpose of the Patient's Charter?

_____

_____

_____

_____

6. Identify three or more ways that beliefs and preferences can affect daily living.

a) The foods they eat.

_____

_____

_____

7. How can you promote equality and avoid discrimination?

_____

_____

_____

_____

8. How can you protect people from abuse?

_____

_____

_____

_____

Module 2

Interacting with Others

Everything you do or say communicates a message.

Objectives:

- ☐ Identify basic needs
- ☐ Outline the basics for positive relationships
- ☐ Use effective communication
- ☐ Identify ways to overcome physical or mental communication barriers

Need-to-know Words:

- · basic needs
- · significant others
- · communication
- · communication barriers
- · aphasia
- · hearing impaired
- · visually impaired

| Part 1 | # Understanding Basic Needs *(O.b.c.e, U4.b.c)* |

Help people feel good about themselves and reach for their dreams.

Everyone has basic needs. When basic needs are not met, people are affected physically, emotionally, mentally, and socially. Common reactions are depression, anxiety, fear, anger, hostility, withdrawal, and physical ailments.

The famous psychologist, Abraham Maslow (1962), identified steps for meeting needs in his Hierarchy of Human Needs. A person's needs must be satisfied at one level before moving upward in a step-by-step progression from basic physical needs toward self-actualisation. Support workers play an important role in meeting people's needs.

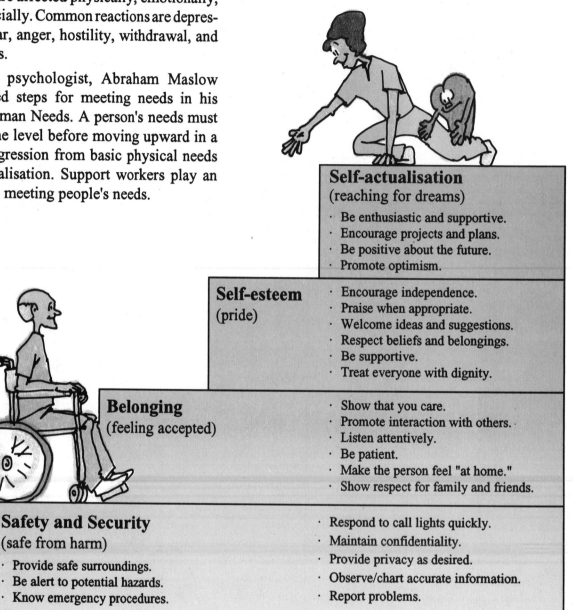

Self-actualisation
(reaching for dreams)
· Be enthusiastic and supportive.
· Encourage projects and plans.
· Be positive about the future.
· Promote optimism.

Self-esteem
(pride)
· Encourage independence.
· Praise when appropriate.
· Welcome ideas and suggestions.
· Respect beliefs and belongings.
· Be supportive.
· Treat everyone with dignity.

Belonging
(feeling accepted)
· Show that you care.
· Promote interaction with others.
· Listen attentively.
· Be patient.
· Make the person feel "at home."
· Show respect for family and friends.

Safety and Security
(safe from harm)
· Provide safe surroundings.
· Be alert to potential hazards.
· Know emergency procedures.
· Respond to call lights quickly.
· Maintain confidentiality.
· Provide privacy as desired.
· Observe/chart accurate information.
· Report problems.

Physical
(survival requirements)
· Provide food.
· Supply fresh water.
· Assist with eating and encourage fluids.
· Assist with elimination as needed.
· Position for comfort and easy breathing.

Part 2	**Building Relationships** *(O.c.d)*

Treating people with respect and dignity builds good relationships.

Good relationships are the foundation for a comfortable working experience. Following are some guidelines for establishing good relationships:

Always knock before entering a person's room. Remember that this is the person's living quarters. Provide the privacy and courtesy you would show to people in their own homes.

Introduce yourself. Some people have difficulty remembering names. Say your name whenever you enter a person's room to avoid confusion or embarrassment.

Ask how each person wishes to be addressed. Many elderly people prefer not to be called by their first names.

Provide comfort. Pay attention to each person's needs. Provide adequate ventilation, warmth, light, and quiet.

Support individual rights and choices within the limits of your work role. Encourage people in your care to express their wishes and needs.

Be courteous and respectful of visitors. Family and friends influence the well-being of people in your care. Provide privacy if desired. If you must give care, politely ask visitors to leave the room, and let them know when they can return.

Maintain privacy and dignity at all times. Everyone wants to be loved and have friends with shared interests. Regardless of age, people are sexual beings with sexual desires. You must deal with sexuality in a mature, professional manner.

Allow people plenty of privacy, and do not interfere with consenting partners as long as no one is in danger of physical harm. If problems arise, ask your manager how to handle the situation.

Offer Choices

Choices encourage independence. Whenever possible, offer choices. For example, your schedule may permit you to give someone a bath now or in 30 minutes. Offer the person a choice, following these guidelines:

- Be specific in your options.

- Stick to your promises.

- Let the person know if you are going to be late.

- If someone is unable to make choices, take the person's interests into account before making a choice for the person.

- Give a clear explanation when a person's request cannot be granted or must be restricted.

- Do not allow yourself or others to be manipulated.

- If you have concerns about offering choices, seek advice from an appropriate person.

Challenging Behaviours *(Z1.b)*

Recognising the link between actions and needs helps build good relationships. Keep in mind that people receiving long-term care are adjusting to changes in their life-styles that affect them physically, emotionally, and socially.

Sometimes people are uncooperative, demanding, threatening, rude, or stubborn. Try to find the underlying cause of the behaviour. Some concerns that affect people's behaviour:

- anxiety
- loneliness
- health problems
- pain
- change in life-style
- loss of independence
- unmet expectations
- fear
- grief
- financial concerns
- longing for the "old days"
- lack of understanding
- unmet physical and social needs
- religious concerns
- family problems
- depression
- lack of self-esteem
- physical and mental changes
- lack of sleep or rest

When challenging behaviours occur, try to defuse the situation so that the dangers and disturbances to others are kept to a minimum. If you require assistance, get help immediately.

If a person in your care exhibits challenging behaviour, follow the plan of care for the person, including any rules or regulations pertaining to the situation. Channel your own emotions into dealing with the situation. Never lose your temper.

Complete any reports of the incident as soon as possible, while events are still fresh in your memory. If you have worries or uncertainties about dealing with difficult behaviours, seek advice from an appropriate person.

Significant Others

Significant others are relatives, friends, or anyone who is important to another person. Sometimes significant others are angry or upset about the illness of their loved one. Even though it may be difficult for you, be understanding and supportive of significant others.

Know who is significant to the people in your care. Assist people with sending and receiving communications. Help arrange visits if possible, and provide a setting that is appropriate for visiting. Encourage visitors to participate in care whenever appropriate (with the person's approval). Provide any training that is necessary.

Do not give out any information that is confidential. Before giving out any other information to visitors, be sure you have permission from the person in your care.

Part 3	**Using Good Communication Skills** *(O.e)*

The way you treat people affects their behaviour.

The ability to communicate well builds good working relations with the people in your care and the care team. Effective communication occurs through a variety of methods, using language that is easily understood by the individual.

Speaking, listening, feedback, and actions affect everything you do for the people in your care:

- provide proper care
- show concern
- get along with the people in your care, their families, and your colleagues
- reduce conflict
- report observations
- give directions
- follow directions
- learn by listening and observing
- send accurate messages
- explain procedures
- define problems

Communication simply means sending and receiving messages. However, effective communication involves more than words. Both verbal and nonverbal messages carry meaning.

Verbal: *Words.* Use simple and clear words that the person easily understands.

Nonverbal: *Body language.* Everything you do sends a message:

- facial expression
- gestures
- tone of voice
- posture
- eye contact
- silence
- touch

Verbal and nonverbal language must agree in order to send clear messages. The problem is that most people are not aware of their nonverbal behaviour. Unless verbal and nonverbal language agree, the listener gets a mixed message. Unfortunately, when messages are mixed, the nonverbal impressions speak louder than the words. For example, if you express concern while standing with your arms folded and a look of disgust, you are sending conflicting messages.

Guidelines for Effective Communication

Communicate with people at their level of understanding. Use an appropriate manner, level, and pace according to individual abilities.

- Convey warmth.
- Show respect with active listening and without passing judgment.
- Convey empathy by reflecting the other person's feelings.
- Show interest.
- Take time to listen.
- Be aware of body language.
- Use a friendly tone.
- Treat the person with dignity.
- Ask open questions (e.g., "how?," "why?")
- Paraphrase (summarise what was said in your own words).
- Ask for clarification.
- Be alert to key words (e.g., "guilty," "hurt") and ask for more information.
- Be concrete and ask for specific examples.
- Point out discrepancies

17

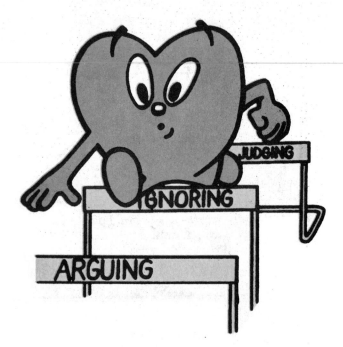

Barriers to Communication

Minimise any barriers to communication. Try a variety of approaches if the message is unclear.

Avoid these barriers:

· being bored or impatient

· threatening or using harsh language

· negating or devaluing the person

· jumping to conclusions

· passing judgment or giving advice

· arguing

· distracting (e.g., fiddling or doodling)

· interrupting

· asking closed questions with single-word answers

· confusing the person with multiple questions

· mumbling

Providing Support

Listening is an important communication skill. You can provide help and support by being an understanding listener. Create a climate in which the person needing help feels accepted and confident enough to be able to talk freely about his or her thoughts and feelings without having to be defensive. As a result of being able to talk freely, the person may gain greater insight into the problem and be able to resolve the problem or cope better with the situation.

Be alert to ways that you can be supportive when someone needs help. The idea is that the person, not you, does most of the talking. Listed below are five types of counselling interviews:

Developmental: helps people confront and deal with specific developmental tasks in their lives. The main emphasis is on development of the person, rather than on specific problems or decisions, e.g., self-awareness.

Problem-focused: helps people overcome or learn to cope better with one or more specific problems, e.g., money problems.

Decision-making: helps people make specific decisions, e.g., choosing a career.

Crisis interviews: help people who feel overwhelmed and are having difficulty coping. The people are often highly emotional, and the counsellor simply works on getting them over the worst of the crisis, e.g., someone has just been made redundant.

Support: occurs when the people are not going through crises, but extra support is needed to help them through awkward phases in their lives.

Part 4 Dealing with Physical Barriers to Communication *(O.e)*

Consider each person's needs and level of understanding.

Various methods of communicating are necessary to support individuals and to interact effectively with them. The methods are based on each person's needs and level of understanding. Modify communication as needed.

The following guidelines will help you interact with residents who have physical barriers to communication.

Aphasia

Aphasia is a loss of ability to speak or understand words. Medical problems can affect the area of the brain that deals with language, making communication difficult and frustrating.

To communicate with people who are aphasic:

- Be patient!

- Use communication aids
  (e.g., pictures, paper and pencil).

- Eliminate unnecessary noises
  (e.g., TV, radio).

- Address the person by name.

- Speak slowly and use simple words.

- Make the message clear, without
  too many details.

- Allow time for the person to respond.

- Be supportive and positive.

- Talk normally; do not "talk down"
  to the person nor shout.

- Ask the person to repeat if necessary,
  rather than to pretend you understand.

Hearing Impaired

To communicate with people who have hearing problems:

- Get close to the person and speak loudly enough to be heard without shouting.

- Speak to the side where hearing is best.

- Maintain eye contact.

- Ask for feedback to determine understanding.

- Eliminate unnecessary noises.
  (e.g., turn off the TV or radio.)

- If the person uses a hearing aid, make sure he or she is wearing it. Be sure the aid is clean.

- Make sure you face the person who reads lips.

- Use gestures.

Visually Impaired

To communicate with people who have vision problems:

- Identify yourself when entering the room.

- Explain what you are going to do.

- Ask for feedback.

- Remind people to wear glasses if they need them, and offer to help clean the glasses.

- Use "touch" when appropriate.

19

Review

1. Why is it important for you to understand basic needs?

_____

_____

_____

_____

2. Identify five or more ways to build positive relationships with people in your care.

a) Treat each person with respect and dignity

_____

_____

_____

3. Why should you knock before entering a person's room?

_____

_____

_____

4. How would you cope with challenging behaviour?

_____

_____

_____

5. Why do you need good communication skills?

_____

_____

_____

_____

6. Describe nonverbal communication.

_____

_____

_____

7. Describe guidelines for effective communication.

_____

_____

_____

8. Describe two or more physical barriers to communication and how to deal with them.

_____

_____

_____

Module 3

Basic Care

Earn the respect of others with good care skills.

Objectives:

- ☐ Explain how to manage information
- ☐ Demonstrate how to weigh and measure people with the standing balance scale
- ☐ Demonstrate how to make a bed
- ☐ Explain how to help people with their personal hygiene
- ☐ Outline how to help people eat and drink
- ☐ Describe benefits of range of movement exercises
- ☐ Demonstrate pressure area care

Need-to-Know Words:
- · managing information
- · observing
- · charting
- · reporting
- · independence
- · hygiene
- · dysphagia
- · feeding tubes
- · range of movement
- · pressure sores

Part 1 — Managing Information *(U5.a.b.c)*

*The care team depends on your accurate and timely information
to manage each person's care.*

An important part of your role is handling and storing records and obtaining information. You need to be a skilled observer, to pass on accurate and timely information, and to maintain confidentiality. If you have any worries or uncertainties about managing information, seek advice from an appropriate person.

Handling Records

Records are important documents that may be in the form of paperwork or electronic data. Be sure to update records accurately and to store them safely so that the records can be retrieved and used in the future. Confidential records must be safely stored when not in use.

To complete or update records, identify that you have the correct records. Be careful to enter accurate data; inaccurate information can be illegal and dangerous.

Note when records are transferred to other locations. Identify where the records were sent so that they can be traced if necessary.

Obtaining Information

Information about care services often needs to be obtained from people receiving care, their families, and from other care workers. Follow these guidelines for obtaining information:

- Be sure that your request for information is appropriate.

- Be clear about the information you need.

- Allow time for the person to respond.

- When necessary, confirm the relevance and accuracy of the information. Seek further information as needed.

- Always safeguard confidential information.

According to internationally agreed principles, collecting personal data requires that information is:

- obtained fairly and lawfully

- held only for one or more lawful purposes specified in the Data Protection Act

- adequate, relevant, and not excessive for specified purposes

- accurate and, where necessary, up-to-date

- kept no longer than necessary for specified purposes

- made available to data subjects on request

- properly protected against loss or disclosure

Observing

Being a skilled observer helps prevent serious problems and earns the respect of your colleagues. Being alert to people and their environment helps to reduce accidents and maintains the well-being of the people in your care. Careful observations increase your awareness of each person's physical, emotional, and social needs.

Learn to recognise signs and symptoms of common diseases and conditions. One of the major keys to helping a person is detecting a problem in its early stages.

> Learn to observe each person throughout your daily contacts.

Watch. Look. Listen. Trust your instincts. If something seems to be wrong, report it. Any physical or emotional changes may indicate a change in the condition of a person's health.

Be alert to physical changes:

- decreased or increased functioning (e.g., elimination, pulse, breathing)
- unconscious, weak, dizzy, trembling
- drowsy, lethargic
- cold, pale, clammy
- hot, sweating, burning, feverish
- nausea, vomiting
- diarrhoea, constipation
- excessive thirst
- odour
- ringing in ears
- blurred vision
- spasms
- pain, difficulty, discomfort
- swelling, oedema
- rash, hives, blisters
- choking, coughing, wheezing, sneezing

Be alert to emotional changes:

- mood swings, loss of control
- depressed, hopeless, crying, tearful
- angry, difficult, irrational
- disoriented, confused
- anxious, frightened, pacing

Charting

The chart is a person's written health record. It is a legal document. Accuracy is very important!

To chart a person's record:

- Write notes on paper first, then check for accuracy and spelling.
- Write clearly and neatly in ink.
- Correct errors by drawing a single line through the error and signing it . Never erase or "white-out" a record.
- Always date and time your record.
- Chart only procedures that you have done, after they are done.
- Chart reports of observations.
- Always sign the entry.
- Keep all information confidential.

Reporting

Thorough and accurate reports are made to the person-in-charge as often as a person's condition requires. End-of-shift reports to the on-coming staff provide the information necessary for continued good care.

Reports should include the person's name and a detailed description of the observation.

Objective reporting means to tell precisely what you see, smell, feel, or hear. If a person complains of symptoms you cannot observe, such as dizziness or pain, report exactly what the person tells you.

Correct: Mrs. Smith said her left ear aches.

Correct: Mrs. Jones' right arm is red, swollen, and warm to the touch.

Subjective reporting is used to report what you cannot sense. You should avoid using subjective reporting. However, if you think something is wrong medically or emotionally, report it to the person-in-charge and chart the report. Report any complaints immediately.

Incorrect: Mrs. Smith has an ear infection.

Correct: Mrs. Smith seems very uncomfortable.

Transmitting Information

Receiving and transmitting information is an essential part of quality care. Accurate information is necessary in order to avoid mistakes or misunderstandings.

Before giving out information, politely check the person's identity and whether the person should have access to the information. When someone requests information, be friendly but do not be afraid to refuse to give information. If the person has the right to know, but you do not have the requested information, quickly find out or refer the person to someone who knows.

To avoid errors, write down any messages immediately and check details for accuracy. Get the information to the intended person within a reasonable time, depending on the urgency of the message.

Be sure the person receiving the message understands the information. If necessary, explain the message so that the person knows what it means.

Part 2 Promoting Independence (U1.a.b.c.d, Y1.a.b.c.d.e, Z13.a.b.)

Help people maintain their independence by focusing on their abilities, not their disabilities.

Promoting independence is one of the main areas of rehabilitation and developmental programmes. It is essential that people are encouraged to be as self-managing as possible, no matter where they live and no matter what their level of ability. Each person's life should be as fulfilling as possible.

Managing A Home

Care services provided in a home vary from person to person. The amount of help and support to manage the home depends on individual needs. The plan of care should be negotiated with the person who is receiving the service whenever possible. His or her preferences should be included in the plan, along with permission to carry out the plan.

Some important aspects of managing a home:

- doing the laundry to maintain a clean supply of personal clothes and linen

- maintaining a clean environment (e.g., dusting and vacuuming)

- carrying out maintenance and repairs

- providing safety and security (e.g., checking for hazards, locking doors)

- preparing and storing food, and ensuring that a balanced diet is available

- shopping for food, household, and personal goods

- managing within a budget

Being Part of the Community

It is important that people are seen out and about in the community if they are to become part of the community. Different people need different amounts of support in the community.

Some important aspects of being part of the community:

- using community facilities (e.g., shops, banks)

- making and maintaining friendships

- taking part in the community's recreational and leisure activities

- being aware of local interests and concerns

Recreation and Leisure

Recreation and leisure activities are essential to a person's well-being and provide a release from the monotony of everyday living. Stimulation from recreational activities is good therapy.

Learn which hobbies, interests, and recreational activities the people in your care prefer. Inform people about recreational options and resources that are available. Let people choose activities, allowing as much independence as possible. Be sure that the chosen activity does not conflict with the plan of care or expose anyone to unnecessary risk.

Provide advice or support as necessary to enable the person to undertake the activity. Evaluate the activity with the person afterwards, and help plan future activities. Record details in the care plan, if appropriate. If you have any concerns about activities, seek advice from an appropriate person.

| Part 3 | **Making Beds** *(Z19.b)* |

A properly made bed adds to a person's comfort and well-being.

Bed making may be part of your daily routine. A properly made bed is free of wrinkles that can cause discomfort and pressure sores.

Making an Unoccupied Bed

1. Gather the linen:
   - top sheet
   - bedspread
   - bottom sheet
   - blanket
   - pillowcase

2. If possible raise the bed to a level that is comfortable for bed making.

3. Unfold and lay the bottom sheet so it hangs evenly on both sides.

4. Tuck the top of the sheet under the mattress.

5. Make a mitred corner:
   - Raise the side of the sheet.
   - Lay it on top of the mattress.
   - Form a triangle.
   - Tuck the hanging portion under the mattress.
   - Bring the triangle down.
   - Tuck under the mattress.

6. Place the top sheet on the bed and mitre the corners at the foot. Do not tuck the bottom under the mattress.

7. Place the blanket, then the bedspread, on the bed.

8. Tuck in the top sheet, blanket, and bedspread together, making mitred corners.

9. Move to the opposite side and repeat, pulling linen tightly to remove wrinkles.

10. Open the pillowcase. Guide the pillow in with seam end first. Do not hold the pillow under your chin!

11. Fold extra material under the pillow.

12. Place the pillow on the bed.

13. Place the call light within easy reach.

Making an Occupied Bed

The method for making an occupied bed is the same as making an unoccupied bed with these exceptions:

1. Obtain help, if needed.

2. Tell the person what you are going to do.

3. Provide privacy.

4. Remove the bed linen, leaving the top sheet to cover the person.

5. Move the person to the opposite side, away from you. **Be sure the side rail is up and locked!**

6. Roll the linen toward the person and tuck the linens under his or her back.

7. Unfold and place clean linen with the centre crease in the centre of the bed.

8. Tuck in with mitred corners.

9. Raise the side rail where you have been working.

10. Move to the opposite side.

11. Lower the bed rail and roll the person onto the clean linens.

12. Remove dirty linen and repeat the process, pulling linen tight.

13. Place the clean top sheet over the person and pull the dirty sheet from below, keeping the person covered.

14. Replace the blankets and bedspread.

15. Change the pillowcase.

16. Position the person comfortably and raise both side rails.

17. Place the call light within easy reach.

Part 4	**Promoting Personal Hygiene** *(Z9.a.b)*

Promote personal cleanliness and appearance.

Help the people in your care to be as self-managing as possible. Some people are able to maintain their own hygiene and appearance. Others need your assistance or guidance.

Offer help that is appropriate to each person's needs, preferences, and beliefs. Always provide care with dignity and privacy. Report any pain, discomfort, or changes in a person's condition to the person-in-charge. Maintain adequate supplies and equipment for everyone's personal use.

Set an example by using good standards for your own personal hygiene and appearance. Be accepting and supportive of others' preferences and beliefs that affect their standards of grooming and clothing.

Mouth Care

Poor mouth care leads to cavities, gum disease, mouth infections, and loss of teeth. Mouth problems may affect a person's ability and desire to eat, resulting in poor nutrition or insufficient fluid intake. Report any redness, sores, or bleeding to the person-in-charge.

Brushing teeth is the most important part of **oral** (mouth) hygiene. Good care extends to the gums and tongue.

Oral hygiene should be done each morning, evening, and after meals. The people in your care should be encouraged to do this for themselves if they are able. Mouth care is given every two hours to people who are unconscious or nil-by-mouth.

Brushing Teeth

1. Wash your hands.

2. Assemble equipment:

   - cup
   - toothbrush
   - mouthwash
   - towel
   - kidney dish
   - toothpaste
   - water

3. Explain what you are going to do.

4. Provide privacy.

5. Hold the toothbrush at a 45-degree angle to the gums and brush teeth thoroughly.

6. Massage the gums by brushing in a circular motion where teeth and gums meet.

7. Brush the person's tongue if requested.

8. Rinse well, and dry the person's mouth.

9. Make sure the person is comfortable.

10. Replace side rails.

11. Report any problems (e.g., swollen gums, irritation, sores) to the person-in-charge.

Denture Care

Some people wear full dentures (false teeth) or partials. As a person ages, mouth tissues change, and dentures may need to be refitted. If a person complains of discomfort or develops mouth sores, notify the person-in-charge.

Remove dentures or partials from the mouth for at least eight hours each day, and store them in liquid to prevent warping. Assist the person as needed to rinse dentures after meals and snacks and to clean them thoroughly once a day.

1. Wash your hands.

2. Assemble equipment:

   - basin
   - denture brush
   - toothbrush
   - drinking glass

3. Tell the person what you are going to do and provide privacy.

4. Remove dentures and soak them in cleaner.

5. With dentures removed, clean the person's mouth. Use a toothbrush to gently clean the tongue, and rinse the mouth thoroughly.

6. Fill the basin with warm (not hot) water, and hold the dentures over the water to avoid breaking if dropped.

7. Use a soft denture brush to clean the dentures. Never use a sharp tool for cleaning.

8. Store dentures in liquid or insert in the person's mouth.

Hair Care

Daily hair care includes brushing and combing. Be sure the person's comb and brush are clean. Comb long, tangled hair one section at a time. Encourage people to care for their own hair if they are able.

Shampoo hair at least once a week. Shampoo during showering if permitted. Assist the person as needed.

1. Wash your hands.

2. Explain what you are going to do.

3. Assemble equipment:

   · shampoo

   · towel

   · conditioner

   · comb or brush

4. Brush hair gently, removing tangles.

5. Adjust the water temperature for comfort.

6. Wet the hair.

7. Shampoo gently, massaging the scalp.

8. Avoid getting soap in the person's eyes.

9. Watch for scalp irritations or problems.

10. Use conditioner if the person desires it.

11. Rinse and dry:

    · towel (pat gently)

    · hair dryer

12. Style in a way the person desires.

13. Make the person comfortable.

14. Clean the equipment.

15. Wash your hands.

16. Report any unusual observations.

Bathing

Bathing provides more than cleanliness. Baths encourage exercise, stimulate circulation, help prevent pressure sores, and promote relaxation. Baths give you the opportunity to spot problems such as infections or sores.

Encourage the people in your care to wash themselves if they are able. Always provide privacy.

Bed Baths

Full or partial bed baths are necessary for non-ambulatory (unable to move or walk) people. Encourage people to help with their baths as much as possible.

1. Assemble equipment:
   - towels
   - soap
   - disposable cloth
   - basin
   - bath blanket
   - clean gown

2. Identify the person and explain what you are going to do.

3. Provide privacy, and close the doors and windows to prevent drafts.

4. Offer toileting.

5. Adjust the bed to a comfortable position.

6. Remove the top bed covers and replace them with a bath blanket.

7. Remove the person's gown while keeping the person well covered with the bath blanket.

8. Fill the basin two-thirds with warm water.

9. Help the person move toward you.

10. Place a towel under the person's farthest arm to keep the bed dry.

11. Make a mitt of the disposable cloth: fold in thirds around your hand, fold the top down, and tuck the bottom end under.

12. Wash eyes from the inner to the outer corner, using water only, and rinse the cloth after each eye.

13. Wash and rinse the person's face, neck, ears.

14. Dry well.

15. Work from the head down, washing with long circular motions, washing, rinsing, and drying thoroughly.

16. Change the water frequently when it is soapy or cool.

17. If the person is able, offer the washcloth for cleaning the perineal area.

18. Turn the person to the side and place a towel on the bottom sheet by the person's back.

19. Wash, rinse, and dry the perineal area (genitalia and rectum).

20. Place a towel under the legs, and bend the knees to wash and dry legs and feet.

21. Apply deodorant or talcum powder as needed.

22. Put on a clean gown.

Safety Guidelines
- Use extreme caution to prevent slips and falls.
- Test the water temperature, then let the person who is going to have the bath test the temperature.
- Assist the person in and out of the bath or shower as appropriate.
- Check with the person-in-charge before you leave a person alone to bathe.

Shower Bath

1. Assemble equipment:

   · towel

   · soap

   · washcloth

   · clean gown or clothes

2. Use a shower chair for safety so the person does not have to stand for long periods.

3. Check the water temperature before the person enters the shower.

4. If necessary, assist the person into the shower.

   · Steady the ambulatory person with your arm.

   · Make sure the wheels on a wheelchair are locked during transfer to the shower chair.

5. Assist as needed in washing, rinsing, drying, and dressing.

General Baths

1. Assemble the same equipment as a shower bath.

2. Fill the bath half full, running the cold water into the bath first. Test the water temperature with a bath thermometer before the person enters the bath. The water should be approximately 38 degrees centigrade.

   If no bath thermometer is available, check the water temperature with your hand, and ask the person who is going to have the bath to check the temperature.

3. Make sure there is a nonslip mat in the bath and at the side of the bath.

4. If necessary, assist the person into the bath.

5. Assist as needed in washing, rinsing, drying, and dressing.

6. If there is any danger of the person falling or slipping while getting into or out of the bath, use a hoist.

Dressing

Some people in your care may need assistance to dress and undress.

1. Tell the person what you are going to do .

2. Wash your hands.

3. Help select appropriate clothing.

4. Prepare clothing by unbuttoning, unhooking, unzipping.

5. Provide privacy.

6. Gently remove clothing one area at a time, keeping the person covered as much as possible.

7. Gently dress the person:

   · Slacks: gather them at the leg, and reach through to guide the person's ankle through.

   · Shirt or dress: gently pull the person's hand through the sleeve.

   · Pullovers: gently guide both arms into the sleeves and slide the garment over the person's head.

8. Smooth the clothing and fasten as needed.

Nail Care

Always check with the person-in-charge before giving nail care. Preferably, a person's nails should be short, smooth, and clean.

Fingernails

1. Wash your hands.

2. Assemble equipment:

   · nail file   · emery board

   · clippers   · towel

   · nail polish   · hand lotion

   · basin of warm water

3. Explain what you are going to do.

4. If nails are thick, soak them in warm water first.

5. Trim torn or rough edges.

6. Fingernails should be rounded.

7. Trim any broken nails carefully.

8. Clean nails carefully with a nail file.

9. Smooth the edges with an emery board.

10. Encourage finger exercises and observe mobility.

11. Apply hand lotion.

12. Apply nail polish if the person desires.

13. Clean the equipment.

14. Wash your hands.

Toenails

Procedures for foot care are the same as hand care with these exceptions:

· Check with the person-in-charge before giving nail care. Some people require care by a chiropodist (e.g., diabetics).

· Check for blisters, sores, corns, infections, or swelling.

· Trim toenails straight across.

· Clean and dry between and under toes.

· Report any foot problems to the person-in-charge.

Shaving

Shaving is an individual choice. Many males prefer a clean-shaven face. Many women desire to shave their legs and underarms. Shave after bathing, when the skin is soft, or use a warm washcloth to soften the skin.

When using an electric razor, be sure the razor is dry and that it belongs to the person who is being shaved.

1. Wash your hands.

2. Gather equipment:

   · razor

   · towel

   · washcloth

3. Explain what you are going to do.

4. Help the person to wash with warm water.

5. Apply shaving cream.

6. Hold the skin taut.

7. Shave in the direction the hair grows.

8. Apply after-shave lotion if desired.

9. Make the person comfortable.

10. Clean equipment.

11. Wash your hands.

| Part 5 | **Enabling People to Eat and Drink** *(Z10.a.b.c)* |

Make mealtimes enjoyable.

Promote self-management as much as possible. Allow time for each person to make appropriate food and drink choices, prepare for meals, eat, and drink. Choices depend on individual preferences and beliefs, dietary needs, and the plan of care. Make sure that each person knows the range of food and drink that is available. Whenever possible, offer suitable alternatives if the person does not like the available choices.

Opportunities should be available for people to help themselves to food and drink at appropriate times. Tell people if they are on special diets, and get their cooperation in keeping to their diets.

Encourage the people in your care to go to the dining room for meals if possible. Dining with others provides an opportunity to socialise.

For people who must eat in their rooms, take a few minutes to chat and make mealtime special. Provide assistance as needed. For people who need extra help, check their care plans to find out if self-feeding programmes have been developed.

Before Meals

Food service requires personal cleanliness for you and the people in your care. Follow these guidelines before serving food:

- Wash your hands.

- Be sure your fingernails are clean.

- Protect any cuts or sores with clean, waterproof plasters.

- Tie back long hair.

- Provide an opportunity for toileting and personal hygiene.

- Offer protection for clothing.

- Provide an opportunity to insert dentures, if necessary.

Some people require very restrictive diets. Before serving food, it may be necessary to check a person's identity by asking the person to tell you his or her name.

Correct:	Please tell me your name.
Incorrect:	Are you Mrs. Smith? (the person may answer in error.)

Serving Food

Be familiar with any special diets for people in your care. Check that the food given to each person is appropriate for the person's diet. When in doubt, ask the person-in-charge. Serving the wrong meal can cause severe health problems.

Follow these guidelines when serving food:

- Present food and drink in an appetising and acceptable manner.

- Be sure the tray has appropriate cutlery, food, napkins, and cup or straw. Provide special eating utensils for people who need them.

- Assist with pouring drinks and cutting food as needed.

- Keep your fingers out of the food and drinks.

Make sure the person is properly positioned for eating, and assist with positioning when necessary. When you are feeding or helping with feeding, sit beside the person at eye level. Offer plenty of liquids, using a straw if the person has trouble drinking from a cup (except for stroke victims).

Follow these feeding guidelines:

- Feed the food slowly.

- Offer small amounts of food at a time.

- Allow time to chew and swallow.

- Watch for signs of gagging or choking!

Dysphagia (difficulty in swallowing) is a problem that can cause severe feeding difficulties. If you observe a person having difficulty swallowing, report it to the person-in-charge.

After Meals

Allow plenty of time for people to finish their meals without feeling rushed. When a person has finished eating and drinking:

- Clear away equipment and left-over food as soon as possible.

- If specified, monitor and accurately record food and drink intake.

- Offer an opportunity for toileting and personal hygiene.

Feeding Tubes

Special tubes are sometimes used for people who have difficulty swallowing. Tubes are ordered only by a doctor and are usually put in place by someone who has received the appropriate training. A nutritionally-balanced liquid diet is fed through the tube.

A nasogastric tube is inserted into the person's nostril and goes into the stomach. A gastric tube is inserted directly through the abdominal wall into the stomach.

Be careful in moving, bathing, or dressing a person with a nasogastric or gastric tube to avoid pulling on the tube. Carefully follow any special instructions, and be alert to any sign of problems:

- Report any signs of discomfort to the person-in-charge immediately.

- Watch for any irritation around the nostril.

- If the tube becomes blocked, report it immediately.

- Keep all food and beverages away from people whose orders indicate nil-by-mouth.

- Always report any unusual observations to the person-in-charge.

| Part 6 | **Weighing and Measuring** (U5.a.b) |

Changes in weight and height may indicate health problems.

Standing Balance Scale

Some people have to be weighed and measured periodically. Accuracy is important. Learn to use the available scales safely and correctly.

The most commonly used scale is the standing balance scale with a measuring rod. For people who cannot stand, there are bed, wheelchair, and mechanical lift scales.

Guidelines for weighing:

- Weigh at the same time of day.
- Wear the same weight of clothing.
- Weigh with an empty bladder.
- Remove footwear.

Weighing

1. Explain what you are going to do.

2. Provide privacy.

3. Place both weights at zero with the balance centred.

4. Assist the person onto the scale.

5. Be sure the person is not holding onto you or the scale, and slide the bottom weight until the balance drops and centres.

6. Add the numbers shown at the weights.

7. Chart the weight.

8. Report any unusual findings or observations.

Measuring

1. Ask the person to turn away from the scale and stand straight.

2. Place the measuring rod against the top of the person's head.

3. Read and record the person's height.

4. If necessary, assist the person in getting off the scale.

5. Report any major changes in height or weight to the person-in-charge.

Part 7	Assisting with Exercises (Z6.a)

Specific exercises help people maintain and improve their mobility.

Long periods of immobility cause contractures (permanent shortening of the muscles) and muscle atrophy (wasting away of muscle tissue). Range of movement exercises help to increase the mobility of joints and prevent contractures and atrophy.

Complications of immobility:

· contractures

· muscle atrophy

· pressure sores

· pneumonia

· urinary problems

· constipation

· deep venus thrombosis

Benefits of exercises:

· prevention of pressure sores by relieving pressure and increasing the blood flow to the underlying tissues (which helps prevent a deep venous thrombosis from forming)

· prevention of urinary stasis, so there is less likelihood of urinary infections or kidney stones

· movement of the chest so that fluid is less likely to collect in one part of the lung and cause infection

· stimulation of the bowels and prevention of constipation

Performing ROM Exercises

Perform range of movement (ROM) exercises only as directed. Exercise one side of the body at a time, working each joint through the normal range of movement. Encourage people to perform the exercises by themselves if they are able.

- Do only the exercises that you know how to do, as detailed in the care plan.
- Help the person understand the reasons for and the nature of the exercises.
- Encourage the person to be as self-managing as possible.
- Give feedback and encouragement to promote confidence and motivation.
- Help the person choose appropriate clothing for exercising.
- Support the joint and move it gently and smoothly through its normal range three to five times.
- Move joints slowly.
- If a joint is red or swollen, do not exercise it until directed by the person-in-charge.
- Never force a joint or move it past the point of pain.
- Watch the person's face for signs of pain.
- If pain occurs, stop the exercises and report the pain to the person-in-charge.

Plan your day to combine tasks whenever possible. For example, a person who does self-oral care also completes range of motion exercises for the arm. As you observe and encourage movement throughout the day, do ROM exercises at the same time whenever possible.

Terms used for ROM exercises:

abduction	moving a body part away from the body
adduction	moving a body part toward the body
extension	straightening a body part
flexion	bending a body part
hyperextension	excessive straightening
dorsal flexion	bending backward
rotation	turning a joint
internal	turning inward
external	turning outward

extension

flexion

hyperextension

Part 8	Providing Pressure Area Care (Z7.c)

Preventing problems is easier than healing damaged skin.

Skin is the body's largest organ, and it is easily damaged. The skin of elderly people tends to be especially vulnerable.

Lying or sitting in one position for too long causes pressure, and pressure affects the blood supply to the skin. Unless skin tissues receive an adequate blood supply, the tissues die.

Preventing problems is much easier than healing damaged skin. Encourage the people in your care to do as much as they can for themselves to minimise the effects of pressure.

Relieve Pressure

· Rotate position every two hours for people who are immobile.

· Use appropriate support pillows to redistribute pressure.

Prevent friction

· Never rub the skin vigorously.

· Avoid dragging a person in bed.

· Avoid wrinkles in the sheets.

Control moisture

· Keep people clean and dry (especially if there is incontinence or heavy perspiration).

Prevent skin trauma

· Keep your nails short in order to avoid accidently scratching people.

· Do not wear jewelry that could scratch or damage the skin.

Pressure Sores

Pressure sores tend to occur over the body's bony prominences. Areas most at risk:

· shoulder blades

· elbows

· hip bones

· sacrum

· knees

· ankles

· heels

Pressure sores develop in four stages.

1. The first sign is a pink or red area of the skin that does not disappear within 15 minutes after the pressure is released.

2. The second stage is cracked, blistered, or broken skin, and the surrounding area is red.

3. In the third stage, skin breaks down and subcutaneous tissue is exposed.

4. In the fourth stage, the sore penetrates to the muscle or bone, and there is infection and drainage of fluid.

Report the first signs of a pressure sore to the person-in-charge immediately!

Part 9 — **Providing Physical Comfort** *(Z19.a.b)*

Help people to be as comfortable as possible.

It is important for people to meet their personal needs for rest. When people do not get enough rest, health problems are liable to develop. Ability to rest can be affected by physical, psychological, social, and environmental factors. Observe each person's physical and mental condition and report any areas of concern.

Promoting Rest

Provide conditions that are suitable for rest. Use appropriate behaviour, movements, and tone of voice to encourage rest.

· Talk to the person and ask what help is needed.

· Adjust light, noise, heat, and ventilation as much as possible.

· Assist the person into a comfortable position which is consistent with the plan of care.

· Help the person carry out any required pre-rest routines or activities.

· If monitoring the person's rest is part of the plan of care, keep accurate records.

· Seek advice from an appropriate person if you have any difficulties in promoting rest.

Minimising Discomfort and Pain

Everyone experiences pain or discomfort at times, but the ability to cope is different for each person. Individual beliefs and cultural background often affect the way a person deals with pain or discomfort (e.g., drugs, yoga, massage, herbal remedies).

Prevent discomfort or pain as much as possible. People should never have to suffer any longer than necessary. Encourage people in your care to use self-help methods if they are able. Whatever method is used must be in accordance with the plan of care.

Follow these guidelines to help minimise physical discomfort for people in your care:

· Encourage people to express feelings of discomfort or pain.

· If monitoring pain or discomfort is part of the care plan, keep accurate records.

· Explain the methods that are available for controlling discomfort.

· Offer support to anyone who is disturbed or upset by another person's pain or discomfort.

· Seek advice from an appropriate person if you have any problems dealing with discomfort or pain.

Review

1. Explain why careful observation is important.

_____

_____

_____

_____

2. Why is confidentiality important?

_____

_____

_____

_____

3. How can you promote independence?

_____

_____

_____

_____

4. Describe three safety precautions when assisting people in bathing.

_____

_____

_____

5. Why is proper bed making important?

_____

_____

_____

_____

6. What should you do before serving meals?

_____

_____

_____

7. Describe five or more ways to support individual beliefs.

a) Show interest in each person's beliefs

_____

_____

_____

8. Describe pressure area care and why it is important.

_____

_____

_____

9. How can you help to minimise discomfort and pain?

_____

_____

_____

Module 4

Elimination

Minimise embarassment and discomfort.

Objectives:

☐ Describe toileting procedures
☐ Explain how to measure fluid intake and output
☐ Describe how to use urine test strips
☐ Discuss common problems of elimination

Need-to-Know Words:

· elimination
· bedpan
· urinal
· bedside commode
· fluid balance
· oedema
· dehydration
· constipation
· impaction
· incontinence

Part 1	**Accessing Toilet Facilities** *(Z11.a.b.c)*

Provide privacy and minimise the person's anxiety.

Elimination is the body's natural process for getting rid of wastes and is essential for the body to function. The person who needs help may be embarrassed. It is your job to be professional, to provide privacy, to minimise anxiety, and to maintain the person's dignity throughout the elimination process.

Using the Toilet

Encourage people to be as self-managing as possible in using toilet facilities (toilets, bedpans, urinals, commodes). Some people need your assistance and support. Assistance should be respectful, sensitive to the person's personal preferences and beliefs, and consistent with the care plan.

- Ask the person to communicate the need to use toilet facilities by any manner that is appropriate.

- Allow the person to choose which toilet facility to use, based on what is available and the plan of care.

- Check with the person to find whether or not help is needed or desired.

- Ensure that the person can call for help if needed, and respond promptly if the person needs help.

- Encourage appropriate cleansing.

- Assist as needed with hand washing.

- Clean toilet facilities for the next person's use.

- Wash your hands.

Discuss any problems of elimination or body waste abnormalities with the person. Report any problems or irregularities to an appropriate person as soon as possible. Complete any necessary records.

Bedpans

When a person is unable to use the toilet, bedpans are an alternative. Bedpans are appropriate for women to urinate (void) and defaecate (bowel movement). Men use bedpans to defaecate and urinals to urinate.

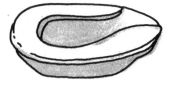

1. Wash your hands.

2. Put on gloves.

3. Assemble equipment:

   · washcloth   · pan and cover

   · toilet   · towel

4. Provide privacy.

5. Pre-warm the bedpan if necessary.

6. Ask the person to bend his or her knees, with feet flat on the bed, and raise the hips. Assist if needed with your hand under the person's lower back.

7. Place the pan.

8. If the person is unable to raise the hips, roll the person away from you, place the pan, and roll the person onto the pan.

9. Raise the person to a sitting position if possible.

10. Cover the person with a sheet.

11. Raise the bed rails.

12. Place the toilet tissue and the call light within easy reach.

13. Ask the person to signal when finished.

14. Never leave anyone on a bedpan for more than 10 minutes; within 10 minutes, check whether the person needs assistance.

15. Remove the bedpan and cover it immediately.

16. Assist with wiping and hand washing as needed.

17. Take the pan to the bathroom.

18. Note any irregularities, and collect a specimen or measurement of output if needed.

19. Dispose of waste matter quickly at an appropriate disposal point to minimise cross-infection.

20. Clean any spillages immediately and thoroughly to prevent accidents and cross-infection.

21. Put bedpan into bedpan washer to be cleaned. (If disposable bedpan liners are available, dispose of the liner after use; clean and store the outer base).

22. Remove and dispose of gloves.

23. Wash your hands.

Urinals

It is common practice for men who are confined to bed to have a clean urinal at the bedside. The urinal is emptied and cleaned after each use (unless it is disposable).

Basic steps that apply to bedpans also apply to urinals.

Bedside Commode

Some people have the ability to get out of bed, but cannot use the bathroom. For those people, there is a bedside commode. The commode is a chair with a hole in the seat and a bedpan below. It is used like a toilet, but the pan must be removed and emptied after each use.

1. Wash your hands.

2. Put on gloves.

3. Assemble equipment:
   · washcloth   · toilet tissue
   · towel   · bedpan

4. Make sure the bedpan is in the commode.

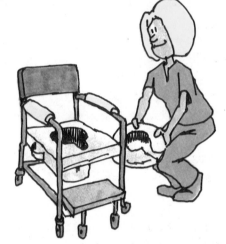

5. Provide privacy, and explain the procedure.

6. Help the person onto the commode.

7. Wash your hands and leave the room.

8. Respond to the call light quickly.

9. Assist with wiping and hand washing as needed.

10. Help the person get back into bed.

11. Cover and remove the bedpan.

12. Observe faeces (waste matter) for blood or other problems, and report any irregularities.

13. Clean the bedpan and store it.

14. Remove and dispose of gloves.

15. Wash your hands.

Part 2	**Charting Fluid Balance** *(U5.b, Z11.c)*

Fluid balance is extremely important to good health.

The doctor or nurse may request that a person's fluid balance be documented. This means recording the amount of fluids taken in and eliminated each day.

Oedema (too much fluid in the tissue) may cause painful swelling and weight gain. Heart and kidney disease, as well as too much salt, can cause oedema. Help make a person with oedema more comfortable:

- Encourage the person to wear loose-fitting clothing.

- Raise the extremity (limb), using a stool or pillow.

Dehydration (too little fluid) may cause weight loss, dry and cracking skin, fever, constipation, and difficulty in swallowing. Help prevent dehydration by encouraging the person to drink fluids.

- Always ensure fresh water is readily available.

- Offer to pour a drink for the person when you enter the room (water, tea, coffee, juices).

- Offer foods such as jelly, ice cream, or custard if the person's diet allows them.

Measuring Fluid Intake

To get an accurate measurement of intake, it is necessary to record all fluids taken by the person. Explain to the person what you are doing and why you are doing it. You need the person's cooperation to ensure that nothing is consumed without letting you know.

Measure fluids taken by mouth as well as soft foods such as ice cream, jelly, or custard. Fluid measurements are recorded in millilitres (mls). Be sure you know how much the containers hold. Qualified staff are responsible for recording intravenous (IV) fluids and nasogastric tube feedings.

- Record intake as soon as it is consumed.

- Record water taken from bedside water pitchers.

- Record between-meal liquid snacks (coffee, tea, or juice).

Measuring Output

Urine is the easiest and most reliable output measurement. Ask the person to let you know before he or she uses the toilet. On the average, a person voids 1200-1500 mls per day.

For anyone who is mobile, a specimen pan is placed on the toilet seat. Ask the person not to empty the pan. For anyone using a bedpan, urinal, or commode, remove the sample to the bathroom.

1. Wash your hands.
2. Put on gloves.
3. Pour the urine into a graduated specimen container.
4. Put the container on a level surface and note the output. Accuracy is extremely important.
5. Observe anything unusual about the urine:
   - blood
   - unusual odour
   - mucus
   - discharges
   - unusual colour
6. Empty the urine into the toilet and flush.
7. Remove and dispose of the gloves.
8. Record the output.
9. Clean all equipment.
10. Wash your hands.
11. Report any irregularities.

Testing Urine

Observe urine for colour, odour, amount, clarity, and frequency. Report any complaints the person has.

You may be asked to do several types of urine tests. Read the instructions carefully if you are unfamiliar with the test.

1. Collect a fresh urine specimen.
2. Put on gloves.
3. Pour a small amount of urine into a clean glass test tube.
4. Dip the test strip into the urine.
5. Wait the set number of seconds as directed for the urine test, then compare the strip to the colour chart on the container.
6. Dispose of used strips and the urine.
7. Remove and dispose of gloves.
8. Wash your hands.
9. Clean and store all equipment.
10. Chart results of the urine test.

Part 3	**Dealing with Problems of Elimination** *(Z11.b)*

Never embarass or scold anyone for having an "accident."

Your reaction to elimination problems is very important. Never embarass or scold people when they lose control. Prevent health problems by keeping people in your care clean and dry.

Bowel Problems

Bowel movements vary from person to person and are affected by medications, diets, fluids, and activity. It is important to observe the frequency, amount, colour, odour, and texture of the stools (faeces). Report any problems related to bowel elimination.

Constipation is bowel elimination that is infrequent and painful with hard faeces. Care includes adjusting the diet, increasing fluids, and more activity. If these measures are not effective, a suppository or enema may be ordered by a doctor.

Impaction is the inability to pass stools. Report any symptoms of impaction immediately:

· pain in the abdomen or rectum

· small amounts of liquid seeping from the anus

· the urge to defecate, but cannot

Incontinence

Incontinence is lack of ability to control the bladder and/or bowels. People who are incontinent should be changed out of clothing that is wet or soiled as soon as possible. Wet or soiled clothing can cause skin irritation, pressure sores, and infections.

It is important for those who cannot regain bowel or bladder control to be seen by a Continence Advisor for advice on continence training, aids, and management.

Continence Training *(X1)*

Training programmes can help people regain control of elimination. If a training plan has been established, follow the instructions carefully. Re-learning bowel and bladder control takes time and patience. Your reaction is very important. Never embarrass or scold people, and keep them clean and dry. You can help people regain control:

· Provide frequent toileting
  (e.g., when the person wakens).

· Encourage plenty of fluids
  (2000 to 2500 mls per day).

· Keep accurate records of intake and output.

· Praise anyone who is making progress.

Review

1. Explain the use of bedpans, urinals, and bedside commodes.

_____

_____

_____

_____

2. What is dehydration, and how can you prevent it?

_____

_____

_____

_____

3. Why is it important for the person in your care to understand procedures for measuring fluid intake and output?

_____

_____

_____

_____

4. Identify five observations for urine.

a) colour.

_____

_____

_____

_____

5. Describe incontinence and how to assist with continence training.

_____

_____

_____

_____

6. Who orders enemas, and why?

_____

_____

_____

_____

7. Why is it important to change wet or soiled clothing as soon as possible?

_____

_____

_____

_____

Module 5

Moving and Positioning People

Safety is the primary concern when moving or positioning anyone.

Objectives:

- ☐ Demonstrate good lifting technique
- ☐ Explain the importance of positioning
- ☐ Demonstrate how to move a person in bed
- ☐ Demonstrate how to transfer a person
- ☐ Describe procedures for change of care environment

Need-to-Know Words:

- · lifting
- · positioning
- · moving
- · transferring
- · transfer belt
- · slide board
- · drawsheet
- · monkey pole
- · hydraulic lift

Part 1	Lifting *(U4.d, Z7.a.b)*

Use good lifting techniques to protect yourself from injury.

Some people cannot or should not move themselves. Moving people is a major cause of accidents and injuries in the care profession. Protect yourself and others from injury by using good lifting technique.

Lifting properly involves how you stand, move, and position your body. Positioning your body -- back, hips, and feet -- in a straight line will prevent injury, and you will not tire as easily.

Use only those lifting and moving techniques that are sanctioned by your employing organisation. Do not do any lifting until you have attended your employing organisation's Lifting Training Course. Update your training if you have any questions or concerns about lifting or moving the people in your care. If you have concerns about the lifting and moving techniques used in your area of work, contact one or more of the following people: your manager, the organisation's Lifting Coordinator (if there is one), your local Health and Safety Officer, your Occupational Health Officer.

Get help before beginning any move if you think you cannot complete the lift or move with the available personnel and equipment. Never risk injuring your back except in rare emergencies (e.g., stopping a person who is falling out of bed). Because of the very real dangers of serious injury when lifting and moving, it is advised that the maximum weights to be lifted are four stones (25 Kg) by a single person, and eight stones (50 Kg) by two people.

Respect people's wishes whenever possible for lifting or changing their positions. Maximise respect and dignity, and minimise any pain, discomfort, or friction from moving. If you need to change the environment for the move, get the person's permission first. Then, return the environment to its original state before leaving the room.

1. Check to be sure that you have the right person.

2. Encourage the person to help with the move and to be as mobile as possible (within the confines of the care plan).

3. Tell the person what you are going to do.

4. Wash your hands before and after lifting or moving anyone.

5. Provide privacy as necessary.

6. Prepare the environment for a safe move or for safe lifting.

7. Wear clothing and footwear that allow you to lift safely.

8. Use appropriate equipment for lifting or moving (e.g., lifting straps).

9. If two or more carers are lifting, one should take the lead to coordinate the actions.

10. After the move, position the person safely and comfortably.

11. Place the call signal, drinks, and other necessary items within easy reach.

The Shoulder Lift

The shoulder lift is the best manual method to move a person up in bed. When there is no other choice (e.g., when a hoist is not available in a person's home) the lift can be adapted to transfer a person from bed to chair or chair to bed. Two or more staff members are required.

The shoulder lift should not be used for people who cannot sit, or for those with shoulder, chest, or upper-back injuries. The procedure below describes how the shoulder lift can be used by two people to lift a person up in bed.

1. Adjust the bed to a height between your hip and knee, and apply the brakes.

2. You and an assistant stand on opposite sides, close to the bed.

3. Help the person to a sitting position.

4. One staff member supports the person while the other adjusts pillows, etc.

5. Stand a little behind the person who is to be lifted, your shoulders level with the person's back. Your inside leg should be kneeling on the bed, at the side of the person being moved, with your knee pointing in the direction of the move. Your outside leg should be placed firmly on the floor with your foot pointing in the direction of the move. Your back should remain straight throughout the lift.

6. Press your nearest shoulder under the axilla, with the person's arms resting on the backs of you and your assistant.

7. Slide the lifting aid under the person's thighs and buttocks and tightly grip the handles.

8. Place your other hand on the bed behind the person, elbow flexed.

9. When the lead staff member signals to lift, extend your rear leg and straighten the elbow of the supporting arm, shifting your weight to the leading leg as you lift.

10. Move the person a short distance at a time, lifting clear of the bed and then bending your leading leg and supporting elbow to lower the person.

Part 2	**Positioning** *(Z7.c)*

Frequent repositioning helps prevent serious health problems.

Frequent positioning and good body alignment aid circulation, relieve pressure, and add to people's comfort. Some people cannot or should not move themselves and need to be repositioned every hour or two. Always check the care plan for frequency of positioning and any restrictions that may apply.

Two major problems for people who are inactive are contractures (tightening of muscles) and decubitus ulcers (pressure sores). Decubitus ulcers are painful and treatment is difficult.

Prevention depends on frequent positioning, good nursing care, and careful observation. Watch for signs of pale or red skin colour at pressure points, and report your observations if the colour does not return to normal after pressure is relieved.

Bed Positioning

Common positions for people who are confined to their beds are prone, supine, and lateral.

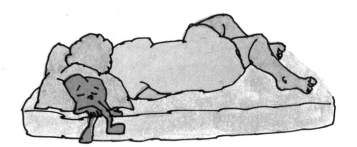

Lateral
(lying on side)

Prone
(lying on stomach)

Supine
(lying on back)

Chair Positioning

Proper alignment and positioning are important for people when sitting. Make sure that everyone has good circulation at all times.

1. Be sure the person's hips are pressing on the back of the chair.

2. Place feet so they are resting comfortably on the floor or on a footrest.

3. Position the back of the knees slightly away from the edge of the chair.

4. If necessary, place a pillow to support the person's lower back.

5. Correct any slumping.

   · If the person slumps sideways, place a pillow on that side for support and to straighten the spine.

   · If the person slumps forward, align the spine by propping pillows on each side or in front.

Part 3	**Moving** *(Z7.a.b)*

Check the care plan for any restrictions before moving anyone.

Prevent friction (rubbing one surface against another) when moving a person. Be careful because friction is painful and can damage the skin.

People who are unable to move themselves need to be turned often in order to prevent physical problems. Roll or slide the person rather than lifting. A variety of turning beds are available. However, if there is no turning bed, the procedure requires two people, one on either side of the bed.

The person should be rolled and slid on a draw-sheet (rather than lifted) by the first assistant, while the other assistant ensures that the person does not roll out of the bed and helps with positioning.

The "golden rule" is to always roll or slide a person toward you, never away from you. Follow the golden rule whenever possible.

To move a person in bed, begin with the person lying on his or her back. Then move the person to one side of the bed in three stages:

1. Move the person's head and shoulders towards the chosen side of the bed.

2. Then move the legs in the same direction.

3. Move the trunk to the side of the bed.

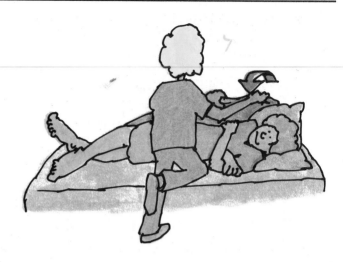

The easiest way to move the trunk of the body is by sliding the person on a drawsheet. You may need an assistant to help you pull the drawsheet if the person is heavy.

If an assistant is not available to help you turn the person, always raise the rails on the opposite side of the bed. This is an important safety precaution to ensure that the person does not roll out of bed.

Begin with the person lying on his or her back on one side of the bed. Then roll the person onto his or her side toward the centre of the bed, following these guidelines:

1. The person's inside arm is positioned to ensure that he is not rolled onto it.

2. The outside leg is crossed over the inside leg.

3. Roll the person onto the side.

Part 4	**Transferring** (U4.d, Z5.c, Z6.b, Z7.a.b)

When transferring people, encourage them to help as much as they are able.

Some people need assistance in transfers (moving from one place to another):

· bed to wheelchair

· bed to commode (portable bedside toilet)

· bed to trolley

· wheelchair to toilet

· wheelchair to bath or shower

· wheelchair to trolley

The pivot transfer is an assistive transfer that is used for people who are hemiplegic (paralysed on one side).

1. Identify the person and explain what you are going to do.

2. Provide privacy.

3. Lock all wheels (bed, wheelchair).

4. Keep transfer sites close together, equalising heights as much as possible.

5. Lower the side rail.

6. Help the person to a sitting position, with feet over the edge of the bed.

7. Stay with the person and allow time to regain balance.

8. Assist with robe and slippers.

9. Stand in front of the person, and put your arms under the person's arms or use a transfer belt.

10. Put the paralysed leg between your knees with your feet wide apart, and place the person's arms around your waist or shoulders (never around your neck).

11. Ask the person to stand while supporting the paralysed leg with your knees and helping maintain balance.

12. Offer reassurance, especially if the person seems concerned.

13. Slowly turn with the person (without twisting), and gently lower the person into the chair.

14. Position the person properly.

To transfer the person back into bed, reverse the procedure. Be sure to raise the side rails and place the call light within reach.

Active Transfer
(moves with minimal help)

Assistive Transfer
(able to help)

Passive Transfer
(unable to help; you need at least one assistant for the transfer)

The **transfer belt** is used when transferring people who are helpless or semi-helpless. Put the belt around the person's waist to provide a grip for you during the transfer. The belt is called a gait belt when used to assist in walking.

The **slide board** is a small board placed between the bed and the chair. The person sits on the board and is helped to slide across the board into the desired position. The slide board is used when there is no danger of spinal injury.

The **monkey pole** is a swinging bar hanging over the bed from a metal frame. The person grasps the bar with both hands and lifts the torso (top of the body) off the bed. The pole may also be used to help people move themselves up in bed, to turn in bed, and to strengthen the arm muscles.

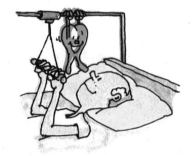

The **hydraulic lift** is used for people who are too heavy to lift. Always have assistance when operating the hydraulic lift. Make sure you understand the operation. Ask the person-in-charge for help if you have any doubt.

The **drawsheet** is used to transfer people when there is no danger of back injury. To transfer a paralysed person, you will need at least one assistant to help you.

Part 5	**Changing Care Environments** *(W3.a.b.c)*

Help people adapt to changes.

It may be necessary to change a person's care environment because the person's care needs have changed. The required service may only be available from another care agency or from another location.

Preparing for the Transfer

Whenever possible, the person should make his or her own arrangements for the transfer. Otherwise, provide whatever help is necessary. Make arrangements for transport or an escort as needed.

Provide appropriate information about the place where the person is going, and answer any questions about the transfer. Some people may not want to leave. Help them overcome their fears and anxieties by carefully explaining the reasons for the transfer. Make the person comfortable and be supportive during the transition.

With the person's consent, inform others who are affected by the transfer (e.g., significant others, family members, care providers). Give the person the opportunity to indicate who is to be the key contact.

During and After the Transfer

Make the transition as smooth as possible when a person transfers from one care environment to another.

· Prepare the new environment for the person's arrival.

· If people are kept waiting, explain the reason for the delay and make them comfortable.

· Observe the behaviour and condition of the person being transferred and any others who are accompanying the person. If there is cause for concern, take appropriate action.

· Encourage questions from the person being transferred and anyone accompanying the person.

· Describe the care that will be provided, including how to summon help.

· Ask whether there are any arrangements to help the person adapt to the new environment.

· Provide a tour of the care environment, if appropriate.

· Introduce relevant others and explain what facilities are available.

· Explain any restrictions or rights of access (e.g., intensive care or security units).

· Inform the appropriate people if any legal conditions are involved in the transfer.

· Monitor the person's adjustment to the new environment.

Review

1. Describe five or more considerations for lifting safely.

   a) Keep my body in a straight line while lifting.

   _____

   _____

   _____

2. Why is good lifting technique important?

   _____

   _____

   _____

3. Why is frequent repositioning important?

   _____

   _____

   _____

4. How do you know when to reposition a person?

   _____

   _____

   _____

5. Which transfer procedures require assistance, and why?

   _____

   _____

   _____

6. When would you use a transfer belt?

   _____

   _____

   _____

7. What is the purpose of the monkey pole?

   _____

   _____

   _____

8. How can you help with the transition when a person moves to a new care environment?

   _____

   _____

   _____

Module 6

Health, Safety, and Emergency Procedures

Simple precautions prevent serious injuries.

Objectives:

- ☐ Discuss accident prevention
- ☐ Identify fire hazards
- ☐ Explain emergency procedures in case of fire
- ☐ Describe the principles of first aid
- ☐ Demonstrate the recovery position
- ☐ Explain how to deal with shock, burns, bleeding, and choking
- ☐ Describe the main areas of health promotion
- ☐ Discuss the Health and Safety at Work Act

Need-to-Know Words:

- · safety hazards
- · emergencies
- · first aid
- · recovery position
- · shock
- · Heimlich Manoeuvre
- · cardiopulmonary resuscitation
- · health promotion

Part 1	**Preventing Accidents** *(U4.c)*

The best way to avoid an accident is to be alert to potential hazards.

Falls are a significant cause of injury. The risk of falling is high for older people, usually due to general weakness, paralysis, confusion, dizziness, impaired vision, or other physical problems.

Before making any changes to a person's immediate environment, ask the person for permission. This is a courtesy as well as a safety factor.

Be alert to safety hazards, and take extra precautions to protect elderly and frail people from injury. Simple precautions can prevent serious injuries.

Preventing Falls

- Remove obstacles to walking such as personal belongings, cords, or equipment.

- Wipe up spills immediately.

- Do not leave a helpless person unattended.

- Keep side rails up.

- Assist people in and out of the bath as necessary.

- Use proper lighting.

- Lock wheels when moving people to and from wheelchairs.

- Keep items that are used frequently close at hand so that the person does not fall reaching for them.

- Answer the call light promptly so the person does not try to get up.

- Encourage people who are unsteady to use hand-rails when walking.

- Assist with walking if needed.

- Be alert to furniture or objects that pose a hazard.

- When moving a wheelchair, do not let the person's feet drag on the floor.

Preventing Burns

- Prevent cigarette burns by enforcing smoking policies.

- Make sure bath water is not too hot. Test the water, and then let the person who is having the bath test the water.

- Assist people with hot foods and liquids.

Accidental Poisoning

Accidental poisoning can be the result of carelessness, confusion, or not being able to read labels because of poor vision. Keep all cleansing agents and disinfectants locked in appropriate storage cupboards.

Choking

- Be sure the person is positioned properly for eating and swallowing.
- Supervise people carefully at mealtimes if they are at risk of choking.
- Encourage people to take small bites and to eat slowly.

Preventing Electrical Shock

- All electrical equipment that is brought into a care facility should be checked by an electrician.
- Inspect all equipment for damage (e.g., frayed cables).
- Operate equipment according to instructions. If in doubt, ask.
- Always use properly earthed equipment.
- Be sure people and areas are dry before plugging in equipment.
- Do not overload circuits.
- Do not use extension cords.

| Part 2 | **Responding to Emergencies** *(U4.e)* |

Save lives by responding quickly.

Principles of First Aid

First aid is emergency care for a person who is ill or injured before medical help arrives. First aid is given to prevent death or to keep injuries from getting worse.

- Act quickly, giving priority to the most urgent conditions.
- Check that there is no further danger to the casualty or to yourself.
- If breathing has stopped, clear the airway and begin cardiopulmonary resuscitation.
- Control bleeding.
- Determine the level of consciousness.
- Guard against shock.

Emergencies happen. Someone's life may depend on you, and you must act *fast!*

- Give reassurance to the casualty and to onlookers.
- Position the casualty correctly.
- If you must move the casualty, immobilise fractures and dress large wounds.
- If needed, get the casualty to hospital for medical treatment as soon as possible.
- Observe carefully for any changes in the casualty's condition.
- Do not try to do too much yourself.
- Ensure that onlookers give you plenty of room.
- Do not give anything by mouth to a casualty who is unconscious or who may need an anaesthetic on arrival at hospital.
- Always record emergency incidents accurately and comprehensively in the prescribed format.

Recovery Position

The recovery position may be necessary to prevent the casualty from choking on the tongue or on vomit, especially if the person is unconscious and lying on his or her back.

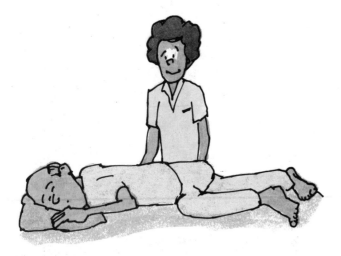

1. Kneel beside the casualty and place both of the person's arms close to his or her body.

2. Turn the casualty gently onto his or her side.

3. Draw the upper arm and leg upwards and outwards to form right angles with the body. This prevents the person from rolling forward.

4. Pull the underneath arm out gently behind the person. This prevents the person from rolling backward.

Shock

All casualties experience a certain amount of shock. It is important for you to recognise the signs and symptoms of shock:

- The casualty feels sick, vomits, or may be thirsty.

- The skin is pale, cold clammy, and may be sweating.

- Breathing becomes shallow and rapid, with yawning and sighing.

- Pulse rate becomes quicker, but weaker.

- Unconsciousness may develop.

Treatment for shock

Treatment is aimed at getting an adequate supply of blood to the vital organs.

- Reassure the casualty.

- Lay the casualty down and raise the legs if possible.

- Place in the recovery position if the person becomes unconscious.

- Keep the casualty warm.

- Loosen tight clothing to help circulation and breathing.

- Moisten the lips if the casualty is thirsty (but do not give anything to drink).

- Avoid moving the casualty unnecessarily.

- Begin cardiopulmonary resuscitation if breathing or heartbeat stops.

- Get the casualty to hospital as soon as possible (unless the casualty has simply fainted).

Burns and Scalds

Burns are generally caused by dry heat, electricity, friction, or corrosive chemicals. Scalds are caused by moist heat (e.g., boiling water).

The pain may be intense, especially with superficial burns. There is usually redness, and blistering often occurs later. There is usually a great deal of shock.

Treatment for burns and scalds

· Immerse the injured area in cold water or place under slowly running cold water for at least 10 minutes. This decreases the spread of heat and alleviates the pain.

· Remove anything that constricts (e.g., rings, clothing, or shoes) before the burned area begins to swell

· Gently remove any clothing that has been soaked in boiling water. (Burnt clothing has been sterilised and does not need to be removed.)

· Lay the casualty down and treat for shock.

· Cover the injured part with a clean, dry dressing.

· Give small amounts of cold drinks at frequent intervals if the person is conscious.

· Arrange for immediate removal to hospital for all but the most minor burns.

· Do not apply any lotions or ointments.

· Do not prick blisters.

· Do not breathe over, cough over, or touch burned areas.

Bleeding

Major bleeding requires immediate treatment to save life. External bleeding is easy to see, but internal bleeding may only show itself as the signs or symptoms of shock. The aim is to control the bleeding and to keep the wound clean and infection-free.

Treatment for bleeding

· Uncover the wound and check for foreign objects. Do not touch any foreign object that is firmly embedded in a wound. Never pull out an object that has created a puncture wound (e.g., a knife).

· If there are no foreign bodies, apply direct pressure to the wound with the fingers and/or hand.

· If the wound is large, squeeze the edges together to try to stop the bleeding.

· Lay the casualty down and treat for shock.

· If the wound is on a limb and there is no fracture, keep the limb raised.

· Place a sterile, unmedicated dressing over the wound, and secure it firmly with a bandage.

· If the bleeding continues, apply additional dressings on top of the original dressing.

· If direct pressure does not stop the bleeding or if there is an embedded foreign body, use indirect pressure before continuing. To apply indirect pressure, press on the main artery that supplies blood to the limb. Do not apply indirect pressure for more than 15 minutes at a time, and do not apply a tourniquet.

· Remove the person to hospital for treatment for all but minor cuts.

The Heimlich Manoeuvre

The Heimlich Manoeuvre is a first-aid procedure for choking. It is used only when there is a complete obstruction (blockage) of the airway.

Clutching the throat is the universal sign for choking. In case of choking, bend the person forward, and give two or three hard slaps between the shoulder blades. Repeat if necessary.

If the person is still choking, proceed with the Heimlich Manoeuvre.

Procedure for Conscious Person

1. Stand behind the person.
2. Slide your arms under the victim's arms and wrap them around the waist.
3. Make a fist and place it against the person's abdomen, below the rib cage and above the navel, being careful not to touch the sternum (breastbone where rib cage meets).
4. Using your free hand, apply pressure against your fist with an inward and upward thrust.
5. Give four rapid thrusts.
6. Repeat the procedure if necessary.

The abdominal thrusts dislodge the food and force it upward, out of the throat.

Procedure for Unconscious Person

If the person loses consciousness from choking, the neck muscles may relax enough that the object no longer completely obstructs the airway. You may be able to remove the obstruction by scooping it out with your fingers.

If the airway is still blocked, use the following procedures:

1. Call for emergency help.
2. Place the person onto his or her back.
3. Open the airway by tilting the head back and lifting the chin.
4. Check for breathing.
5. If there is no breathing, open the mouth and try to sweep the mouth with your finger to remove the blockage (use a scooping motion rather than pulling).
6. Pinch the nose closed and ventilate (give air) through the mouth with two full breaths.
7. If the airway is still blocked, kneel beside or straddle the person at hip level.
8. Place the heel of your hand on the person's abdomen below the rib cage with your fingers pointing toward the person's chest.
9. Place your free hand over the positioned hand.
10. Place your shoulders over the person's abdomen and press your hands inward and upward.
11. Give six to ten rapid thrusts.
12. Check to see if the obstruction is dislodged.
13. Try to sweep the object out with your scooped fingers.
14. Repeat steps 6 to 11 if necessary.

Cardiopulmonary Resuscitation (CPR)

CPR training teaches valuable lifesaving skills, using mouth-to-mouth resuscitation and chest compression when the heart and/or lungs have stopped working.

Only fully-trained people should administer CPR. If you have not already had a course in CPR, check with your instructor for classes in your area.

Quick action is critical. CPR is first-aid emergency care until medical help arrives. CPR must begin as soon as the heart stops in order to prevent brain and organ damage.

The following information is not a CPR course. It is intended as a basic review for those who have completed CPR training.

1. Call for help.

2. Shake the victim (unless you suspect spinal injury), and call the person's name.

3. If there is no response, check for breathing.

   · **Look:** for chest movement.

   · **Listen:** by putting your ear near the victim's nose and mouth.

   · **Feel:** for breath on your cheek.

4. If there is no breathing, begin artificial respiration (you artificially breathe for the person).

5. Use precautions to prevent infection. (Remember you are potentially at risk from all people.)

6. Tilt the head back by lifting the neck.

7. Pinch the nose closed to prevent air from escaping through the nostrils, and cover the victim's mouth completely with your mouth.

8. Blow into the person's mouth until you see the chest rise.

   · Blow two full breaths, and turn your head to the side to listen for air.

9. Check the carotid pulse (5 to 10 seconds). If there is no pulse, begin to artificially pump the victim's heart.

   · Be sure the victim is lying flat on a hard surface.

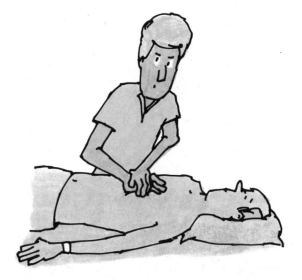

   · Locate the lower end of the victim's sternum.

   · Place the heel of your lead hand over the end portion of the person's sternum, and place the heel of your other hand over the top for leverage.

   · Use the heels of your hands to compress the chest 15 times.

10. Continue to give two breaths followed by 15 thrusts until medical help arrives.

Note: If there are two people available from the outset, they should work together. The requirement is one breath to five chest compressions.

Part 3	Promoting Fire Safety *(U4.c)*

People depend on you for their safety.

Fire can be a panic situation for a person who is confined to a wheelchair or bed, or for anyone who has reduced mobility.

> In case of an emergency, stay calm and take immediate action to remove people from danger.

Recognising Hazards

Awareness of fire hazards is the first step toward prevention. Three elements are needed for a fire to start. By removing any of these elements, a fire can be prevented:

heat:	flame or spark
oxygen:	normal air
fuel:	any combustible material (items that catch fire and burn easily)

Alert the person-in-charge if you smell smoke or if a door feels hot. **Do not open the door!**

Smoking

Never leave smokers unsupervised. Some people may not be able to handle smoking materials safely because of medications or reduced abilities.

Smoking materials should be stored for safe keeping. Strictly follow the smoking policy:

- Smoking is allowed in authorised areas only.
- Use noncombustible ashtrays.
- Be careful when you empty ashtrays.
- Never use paper cups or rubbish bins for ashtrays.
- **Never permit smoking where oxygen is in use.**

Storage

Never store oily rags, paint cans, chemicals, or other combustibles in closed areas.

Faulty Wiring

Inspect all equipment that you use and report any defects. Do not use faulty equipment:

- frayed power cords
- overloaded circuits
- overheated equipment
- improperly earthed equipment

Aerosol Cans

Never burn aerosol cans. Never use an aerosol spray near open flames or cigarettes. The container may explode.

In Case of Fire

Be sure you know the organisation's fire emergency procedures:

· Understand fire and evacuation procedures.

· Know the location of all exits.

· Know where the fire alarms and extinguishers are located.

· Know emergency telephone numbers.

In case of fire, remember:

ARCE

Alarm

Rescue/Evacuate

Contain

Extinguish

1. Sound the **alarm.**

2. **Evacuate** the premises and rescue any people in immediate danger if it is safe to do so.

3. **Contain** the fire by closing doors and windows.

4. **Extinguish** the fire, if possible, using the correct extinguisher.

Fire Extinguishers

Different types of extinguishers are used for different types of fires. Be sure you have the correct extinguisher for the fire!

Water (red)	for most fires, except those involving flammable liquids or live electrical apparatus
Foam (cream/yellow)	for burning liquids or electrical fires
Powder (blue)	for burning liquids or electrical fires
CO_2 Gas (black)	for burning liquids or electrical fires
Halon (green)	for electrical fires
AFFF (cream/yellow)	for general fires, burning liquids or electrical fires; use as directed for water or foam, depending on the type of fire.

Part 4 — Promoting Health (U4.a, W8.b)

Promote health, reduce harm, and control infection.

You contribute to the health, safety, and security of people in your care in three main areas:

· promoting health

· reducing harm

· controlling infection

All care agencies have organisational policies that outline how to provide health promotion and advice. Health promotion plays an important role in the delivery of care:

· maintaining an environment that is clean and safe

· encouraging exercise and mobility

· ensuring a healthy diet

· promoting adequate sleep and rest

· encouraging recreational and leisure activities

Promote health and offer advice in an acceptable manner. Encourage the people in your care to ask questions. If you cannot answer a question, admit that you do not know the answer; refer the person to someone who can answer the question. Respect a person's right to ignore health advice.

Health promotion materials should be available in the care setting. Materials should be relevant and up-to-date, with different language versions available if necessary.

Your behaviour and appearance in the care setting are important factors in promoting health and well-being for others. Set a good example:

· Maintain appropriate weight; avoid being overweight.

· Practice good personal hygiene.

· Wear appropriate clothing and/or protection.

· Maintain your own physical and mental health; look healthy.

Part 5   Understanding the Health and Safety at Work Act *(U4.b.c.d)*

Maintain an environment of health, safety, and security.

The Health and Safety at Work Act (1974) identifies responsibilities for the employer, employee, and management.

Employee Duties

- Care for the health and safety of self and others.

- Comply with the requirements imposed on the employer.

- Never interfere or misuse anything provided for health, safety, or welfare.

- Adhere to instructions in the operation of plant and equipment.

- Use materials only according to recommended procedures.

- Use protective clothing and equipment as provided.

Employer Duties

- Ensure health, safety, and welfare at work for all employees.

- Provide and maintain equipment and systems that are safe and without health risks in the use, handling, storage, and transport of articles and substances.

- Provide information, instruction, training, and supervision for health and safety at work.

Management Responsibilities

- Maintain a safe environment for all staff.

- Ensure that staff adhere to orders and procedures.

- Provide training for safe practices and work methods.

- Explain hazards and safe practices to new employees in the department before they begin their work.

- Report/record all accidents.

Safety and Security Guidelines

- Maintain an environment of health, safety, and security based on individual choices that are consistent with organisational policies.

- Take appropriate action immediately whenever a person's health, safety, and security are threatened.

- Establish rights of entry before allowing callers to enter the premises.

- Carefully explain any restrictions on a person's freedom to the people involved.

- Encourage people to keep their personal belongings in a secure, appropriate place.

- Follow organisational procedures for securing cash and valuables.

- Dress, behave, and practice personal hygiene in keeping with good health and safety practices, including use of appropriate protection where necessary.

- Record any incidents carefully and comprehensively in accordance with local and national policies, and inform your manager.

- If you have any concerns about health, safety, or security, seek advice from an appropriate person.

Review

1. Identify six or more ways to prevent falls.

    a) Wipe up any spills immediately.

    _____

    _____

    _____

    _____

2. How can you prevent accidental poisoning?

    _____

    _____

    _____

    _____

3. Identify potential safety hazards.

    _____

    _____

    _____

    _____

4. Explain the Heimlich Manoeuvre and when you would use it.

    _____

    _____

    _____

    _____

5. When would you use CPR?

    _____

    _____

    _____

    _____

6. What would you do in case of fire?

    _____

    _____

    _____

    _____

7. Give four or more examples of ways to promote health.

    _____

    _____

    _____

    _____

Module 7

Infection Control

Treat everyone with care and caution.

Objectives:

- ☐ Discuss precautions to control the spread of infection
- ☐ Describe ways to prevent infection
- ☐ Explain the importance of hand washing regularly
- ☐ Discuss the need for protective barriers
- ☐ Explain how to control HBV
- ☐ Identify ways that HBV and HIV are transmitted

Need-to-Know Words:

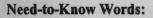

- · infection
- · precautions
- · micro-organisms
- · pathogens
- · sterilisation
- · disinfection
- · isolation
- · asepsis
- · protective barriers

Part 1	**Using Precautions** (U4.d)

Protect against possible infection at all times.

Infection control is a major concern for care workers. Precautions were developed in 1988 to prevent the spread of deadly blood-borne viruses and bacteria.

Precautions establish safe practices for care workers to control the spread of Acquired Immune Deficiency Syndrome (AIDS) and Hepatitis B Virus (HBV). Because you do not know who is infected, you need to use precautions with everyone.

Precautions

Treat everyone with care, but use precautions with each person, all used needles, and all body fluids. Assume all are potentially infectious. Gloves must be worn at all times when handling these materials to avoid infection.

Infected people often have no symptoms and may not know they are infected. Therefore, consider yourself at risk of infection from everyone.

Faeces (body waste), urine, sweat, vomit, or nose and mouth secretions are sources of cross-infection (infection passed from one person to another).

Gloves

Always inspect gloves before use. Do not use gloves that are torn or cracked, have holes, or are faded. Always wear gloves when you:

- handle blood or body fluids

- tend people with pressure sores, broken skin, rashes, or bleeding

- handle linen soiled with blood or other body fluids

- clean up spills containing blood or body fluids

Needles

Everyone who handles needles must use extra caution.

- Be aware that the gloves will not protect you from needlesticks.

- Dispose of needles in proper disposal containers.

Other Precautions

- If you are pregnant and working in a high-risk area, seek advice from your manager.

- Report all broken skin contact, mucous membrane contact, and puncture wounds.

- Wash hands after disposing of gloves.

Part 2 — Preventing Infection (U4.a.c.d)

Preventing problems is better than correcting mistakes.

Infection control is critical! By understanding how infection spreads, you can protect yourself and others.

To protect others from infection, it may not be appropriate for you to work if you have an infection (e.g., the common cold). If there are no clear guidelines, ask the person-in-charge. Notify your manager immediately if you are ill with a notifiable disease (e.g., measles).

Steps for controlling infection:

· Protect everyone from infection by others.

· Prevent reinfection while recuperating.

· Provide surroundings free of disease-causing germs.

Infection is spread by micro-organisms (living germs that can be seen only with a microscope). Micro-organisms are everywhere--in the air, on the skin, in food and beverages, and on everything you touch.

There are two types of micro-organisms:

· non-pathogenic (harmless)

· pathogenic (harmful)

Pathogens are spread in five ways:

· through the air

· direct personal contact (touching the person)

· indirect contact (touching contaminated objects)

· through food, water, or blood

· from people, animals, or insects (sneezing, coughing, touching animals)

Micro-organisms that cause disease are:

· bacteria
    e.g.,   staphylococci (staph)
            streptococci (strept)

· virus

· fungus

Always report signs of infection:

· fever	· chills
· restlessness	· lack of appetite
· swelling	· redness
· pain	· discharge
· change in behaviour	

Infection usually enters the body through broken or damaged skin, or through the mucous membranes of the eyes, nose, or air passages.

Keeping Surroundings Clean

Help control infection with clean surroundings. Keeping the surroundings clean includes cold sterilisation, disinfection, proper linen handling, and isolation.

Sterilisation

Sterilising kills bacteria. Unless **all** bacteria are dead, an object is not sterile. A sterile object becomes contaminated when exposed to air or other objects. Diagnostic equipment and metal bedpans are most commonly sterilised by autoclaving (an intense heat process).

Disinfection

Disinfecting requires chemicals that kill most of the bacteria. Those that are not killed are slowed in their growth. Reusable plastic bedpans, urinals, and equipment are sanitised (washed in a bacterial cleanser), dried, and stored in clean paper bags.

Linen Handling

Use precautions when handling linen to prevent infection from spreading.

· Hold linen away from you to prevent transferring micro-organisms.

· Avoid shaking or fluffing linen, and keep linen off the floor.

· Wear gloves to handle linen that is soiled with blood or body fluids.

· Place soiled linen in covered hampers or bags to prevent the spread of infection and to control odours.

· Always wash your hands after handling soiled linen.

Isolation

Isolation (setting apart) procedures are used when extra precautions are necessary to control the spread of infection.

People with contagious diseases are sometimes isolated to protect others from being infected. Isolation may also be ordered for people who cannot fight infection because of age, illness, or medications. Doctors order isolation precautions, which vary according to the specific problem. It is very important to follow the doctor's orders.

Signs are posted on the door requiring visitors to report to the person-in-charge before entering. Depending on the type of infection, surgical gowns, gloves, and masks may be required.

All basic supplies and equipment for the care of the isolated person should be stored in the room. Gather any additional equipment before you put on a gown or enter the room.

It is not uncommon for an isolated person to become depressed. You can help ease depression in a variety of ways:

· Answer the call light promptly.

· Care for the isolated person first.

· Tell the person when you will be back; be prompt or let the person know if you are delayed.

· Be cautious of what you say outside the room; the person may hear you.

· Help the person, the family, and visitors to be comfortable and confident with the isolation procedures.

· Provide puzzles or other amusements.

Part 3	## Washing Your Hands (U4.d)

Hand washing is the most important preventive measure for infection control.

The spread of infection is greatly reduced by medical asepsis (procedures to decrease disease-producing micro-organisms).

Medical asepsis includes:

· hand washing

· clean surroundings

· personal hygiene

Control infection by washing your hands:

· before and after your work shift

· before and after meals

· before and after providing care

· after using the toilet

· after coughing, sneezing, or blowing your nose

· after handling bedpans or specimens

· after handling soiled linen

Part 4	## Using Protective Barriers (U4.d)

Protective equipment is a barrier between you and the sources of infection.

Protective Equipment

Protective equipment such as masks, gloves, and gowns should be worn whenever you might be exposed to blood or bodily fluids.

Always wear medical gloves whenever you have contact with any of the following:

· people who are bleeding or have open wounds (e.g., pressure sores, skin rashes, or broken skin).

· blood or other body fluids.

· soiled linen.

Putting on Gloves

- Check for cracks, punctures, tears, or discoloration.

- Discard if damaged.

- Check for proper fit.

- Pull the gloves over gown cuffs if a gown is worn.

Removing Gloves

- Hold at the cuff and pull inside out.

- Fold the second glove off the hand over the first glove, enclosing the first glove within the second.

- Dispose of gloves, using the designated bin for infected waste.

- Wash your hands.

Part 5   # Controlling Hepatitis B Virus *(U4.d)*

Vaccination can prevent HBV infection.

Hepatitis B Virus (HBV) is a viral infection of the liver. It produces fatigue, mild fever, muscle and joint pain, nausea, vomiting, and loss of appetite.

There is no known cure for HBV. A blood test is the only way to find out if you are infected. HBV usually spreads through contact with infected blood, blood products, and bodily fluids. However, the virus can be found in urine, faeces, semen, tears, saliva, vaginal fluid, and breast milk.

The virus is transmitted primarily through:

- intimate sexual contact

- puncture wounds from contaminated needles or sharp objects

- mucous membranes (eyes, nose, or mouth)

- damaged skin (cuts, rashes, dry skin)

> Be tested for HBV. If you test negative, get vaccinated to protect yourself from infection.

Part 6	**Dealing with AIDS** (*U4.d*)

Care workers must take special precautions with body fluids, especially blood.

Acquired Immune Deficiency Syndrome (AIDS) is caused by the virus HIV (human immuno-deficiency virus). AIDS cripples the immune system (the body's natural defense against disease), and the person eventually dies from infections.

AIDS kills! Prevention is the only cure. The best attack against AIDS is to be well informed. Find out all you can about AIDS. Use preventive measures to protect yourself and others from infection.

The HIV virus is passed on in exactly the same ways as the Hepatitis B Virus. People are unlikely to become infected from casual contact.

People at high risk are those who have:

· unprotected sex

· many sexual partners

· other sexually-transmitted diseases

· injected drugs and shared needles

· had blood tranfusions since 1977
  which were not heat treated

Since 1985, all donated blood in the United Kingdom has been tested for antibodies to HIV. Unfortunately, some haemophiliacs who were treated with clotting factor before 1985 have developed AIDS.

When people are infected with HIV, they are carriers for life. Some carriers never show symptoms, but can still transmit (pass on) HIV to others.

Treat everyone with care and caution. Use precautions with everyone since you do not know who might be infected.

Some people develop mild symptoms of the disease a few days after infection:

· flu-like sickness

· swollen glands

· rash

· fever

These symptoms go away, but the HIV remains in the body. There is no known cure and no vaccine for HIV. Advanced symptoms may develop five to fourteen years later.

The disease is transmitted when contaminated (infected) fluid enters the bloodstream.

How HIV is transmitted:

· blood

· body fluids that contain blood

· semen

· vaginal secretions

(Of these, blood is the most common concern for health-care workers.)

How HIV enters the body:

· puncture wounds from infected needles
  or broken glass

· cuts or open sores

· mucous membranes (nose, mouth, eyes)

· intimate sexual contact

· transfusions with infected blood

· infected hypodermic needles

· infected mothers to their unborn babies

Review

1. What precautions apply to care workers?

_____

_____

_____

_____

2. What is the difference between sterilising and disinfecting?

_____

_____

_____

_____

3. Give five or more examples of when you must wash your hands.

a) *After coughing, sneezing, or blowing my nose.*

_____

_____

_____

4. Give three or more examples of when to wear gloves.

_____

_____

_____

_____

5. Explain isolation procedures.

_____

_____

_____

_____

6. How can you protect yourself from Hepatitis B Virus?

_____

_____

_____

_____

7. Identify three or more ways that HIV infection is spread.

_____

_____

_____

_____

8. Who is at high-risk for AIDS?

_____

_____

_____

_____

Module 8

Taking Vital Signs

Accurate measurements help determine a person's condition.

Objectives:

- ☐ Name three vital signs
- ☐ Describe how to take an oral temperature
- ☐ Explain the procedure for taking a pulse
- ☐ Discuss how to count respirations

Need-to-Know Words:

- · vital signs
- · temperature
- · pyrexia
- · hypothermia
- · pulse
- · respiration

Part 1	Taking a Temperature *(U2.b/U5.a.b)*

Body heat provides important health information.

Temperature, pulse, and respiration are called vital signs. You need to know how to measure vital signs. Accurate measurements provide important health information for proper care.

Vital signs often have to be taken regularly, at set times, to monitor a person's physical condition. It is important that you take the readings at the correct time of day.

Temperature refers to body heat and is usually measured with a glass thermometer. The thermometer has two parts:

- bulb (the part that contacts the person's body)

- stem (the part showing the display)

Glass thermometers are hollow glass tubes filled with mercury (a liquid). The stem is calibrated (marked) in degrees and fractions of degrees. Care must be taken not to drop glass thermometers because they break easily.

> Always inspect the thermometer and never use one that is chipped or cracked.

Never clean a glass thermometer with hot water. The mercury will expand and the thermometer may break.

> **Caution:** Mercury is poisonous and can be absorbed through the skin. Always use special care in cleaning up broken glass thermometers!

Two body areas for measuring temperature and the average range in degrees Celsius are:

oral (mouth)   36-37° C

axillary (armpit)   35.5-36.5° C

A **pyrexia** is a temperature above 37.5 degrees centigrade, usually due to an infection.

A **hypothermia** is a temperature below 35 degrees centigrade, usually due to being exposed to cold environment.

Oral Temperature

An oral temperature is taken when a person has no difficulty holding a thermometer in the mouth. Never take an oral temperature if a person:

- cannot breathe with mouth closed

- is unconscious

- is six years or younger

- has seizures

- is on oxygen

- is confused or is likely to bite the thermometer

Procedure

1. Wash your hands.

2. Inspect the thermometer for chips and cracks.

3. Take a firm grip on the thermometer by the stem (never touch the bulb), and shake the mercury down the stem into the bulb.

4. Place a disposable sheath over the stem.

5. Tell the person what you are going to do and why.

6. Gently insert the bulb end under the person's tongue.

7. Ask the person to keep the lips closed.

8. Leave the thermometer in place for at least three minutes.

> Never leave a person unattended with a thermometer in place.

9. Remove and read the display.

10. Evaluate the reading. If it seems low, retake the temperature, after shaking down the thermometer.

11. Discard the disposable sheath.

12. Record the temperature legibly and accurately in the person's chart.

13. Report major changes from previous readings to the person-in-charge.

14. Wash your hands.

Axillary Temperatures

Follow the same procedure as an oral temperature with these exceptions:

- Place the thermometer in the centre of the axilla (armpit).

- Put the person's arm across his or her chest to hold the thermometer in place.

- Keep the thermometer in place for 10 minutes before taking a reading.

Temperature Strips

Several companies manufacture temperature strips for taking temperatures. The strip is usually held in place, (e.g., on the forehead) and the colour of the strip is compared against a colour chart to derive a person's temperature.

Part 2	**Taking a Pulse** (U5.a.b)

As the heart beats, it pumps blood into the arteries,
causing them to expand and contract.

The heart's contractions (pulse) are measured to determine how fast the heart is beating. The average range for adults is 56-80 beats per minute (bpm).

Three observations you should make when taking a pulse:

- **rate** (number of beats per minute)

- **rhythm** (how regular and even the beats are)

- **strength** (weak or pounding)

The pulse can be felt easily at the points of the body where the arteries are closest to the skin. The two most common points are radial and carotid.

Radial (thumb side)

The wrist is where the **radial pulse** (from the radial artery) is felt. If the pulse is very weak, take a reading from the other arm for comparison.

Carotid

The **carotid artery** is in the neck, next to the Adam's apple, and can be felt when the pulse is too weak to feel at the wrist.

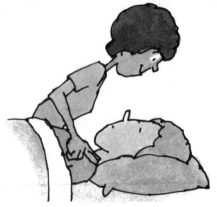

Other Pulse Sites

- temporal (side of head)

- brachial (inside upper arm, above elbow)

- femoral (groin)

- popliteal (knee)

- pedal (top of foot)

Procedure

1. Measure the pulse when the person is at rest. (Exercise, fever, emotions, or pain can increase the pulse rate.)

2. Locate the pulse.

3. Using a watch with a second hand, count the beats for one full minute.

4. Record the pulse count.

5. Report major changes from previous readings to the person-in-charge.

Part 3	**Counting Respirations** *(U5.a.b)*

Changes in breathing may be a warning sign of respiratory problems.

Each respiration (breath) has two parts:

· inspiration (breathing in)

· expiration (breathing out)

To count respirations, watch or feel the person's chest rise and fall. Try to observe respirations without the person's awareness to prevent any anxiety that might cause a change in the normal rate. If possible, observe respirations while carrying on a conversation.

Some causes of increased respiration:

· fever

· exercise

· stress

· disease

· medications

Some causes of decreased respiration:

· medications

· disease

Adults average 16-20 respirations per minute. Pay special attention to respirations that are:

· very fast or very slow

· noisy (describe the sound)

· shallow (very little chest movement)

· rapid

· laboured (wheezing with great effort)

· irregular

Notify the person-in-charge of any irregularities in breathing.

Review

4. Identify the two most common areas for measuring the pulse.

_____

_____

_____

_____

_____

1. What is the normal range of an oral temperature?

_____

_____

_____

_____

_____

5. What are three observations to note while taking the pulse?

a) Whether the beats are strong or weak.

_____

_____

_____

2. What is the normal range of an axillary temperature?

_____

_____

_____

_____

6. Identify three or more causes of increased respiration.

_____

_____

_____

_____

3. Why is it so important to inspect glass thermometers before using them?

_____

_____

_____

_____

7. What could cause decreased respiration?

_____

_____

_____

_____

Module 9

Sensory and Mobility Aids

Help people maintain their independence by focusing on their abilities, not their disabilities

Objectives:

☐ Demonstrate general care for sensory and mobility aids

☐ Explain general care for hearing aids

☐ Explain the care of glasses and artificial eyes

☐ Identify four mobility aids

☐ Describe how to check mobility aids for wear

Need-to-Know Words:

· sensory
· mobility
· prosthesis
· hearing aid
· wheelchair
· cane
· Zimmer frame
· crutches

| Part 1 | **Caring for Sensory & Mobility Devices** *(U2.b)* |

Sensory and mobility devices help people rely more on themselves and less on others.

Sensory and mobility aids contribute to a person's well-being and independence. Aids include glasses, hearing aids, Zimmer frames, canes, and wheelchairs.

Some people wear prostheses. A prosthesis is an artificial substitute for a missing body part such as an arm, leg, breast, or eye.

Proper care and use of aids and prostheses are important:

- Know the correct way to use a device before helping someone else use it.

- Make sure the person knows how to use the device.

- Inspect the device before and after use, making sure it is in good condition. DO NOT let anyone use a defective device.

- Keep the person's equipment within easy reach.

- Check for any physical problems that might develop with use (pinching, swelling, rubbing, sore spots).

- Keep the device properly cleaned.

- Schedule regular maintenance.

- Mark the person's name in an inconspicuous place for identification.

- Mark the removeable foot pedals on wheelchairs.

- Encourage people to help with the care of devices if they are able.

| Part 2 | **Caring for Hearing Aids** *(U2.b)* |

Hearing aids are fragile and require special care.

Be extra cautious when handling hearing aids because they are fragile. Dropping an aid can cause damage. Avoid accidently dropping an aid by using a table or desk for cleaning the aid or changing batteries.

Keep hearing aids dry; water ruins them.

- Remove hearing aids before showering or swimming.

- If the hearing aid gets wet, dry it with a soft cloth; never use heat.

Keep hearing aids clean.

· Never use water, alcohol, or cleaning solvents.

· Remove the aid before using hair spray.

· Use a soft cloth.

· Never use oil.

Extend the life of batteries; they are expensive.

· Turn off the hearing aid when it is not in use.

· Open the door to disconnect the battery contact for nighttime storage.

· Remove the battery if the aid will not be used for over 24 hours.

· Check to be sure the battery is working before placing the aid in a person's ear.

Store hearing aids in a safe place.

· Always use a case for storing the hearing aid.

· Mark the case with the person's name.

· Never leave the aid within reach of visiting children.

· Discourage the person from putting the aid in a pocket; it may go to the laundry with the clothing!

Hearing Aid Trouble Shooting

Problem	Possible Cause	Action
Doesn't Work	dead battery plugged earmold	replace battery clean earmold
Not Loud Enough	low battery plugged earmold hearing may have changed	replace battery clean earmold have hearing checked
Distorted	low battery	replace battery
Fuzzy	faulty hearing aid	check with supplier
Goes On and Off	bad battery faulty hearing aid	replace battery check with supplier
Causes Discomfort	improperly placed wrong style	check placement check with supplier

Part 3	Caring for Glasses and Artificial Eyes *(U2.b)*

Protect glasses from damage or loss.

Glasses

Glasses are often misplaced and easily broken. Encourage people to wear glasses if they need them.

To prevent damage or loss:

· Engrave the person's name on the inside of the frame.

· Make sure the person has a case for storing glasses. A second case may be needed to carry glasses during the day.

· Provide a neckstrap to keep glasses on the person.

· Clean glasses with a soft cloth rather than with a paper tissue which could scratch the lenses.

· Check glasses often for loose screws or broken nosepieces.

Artificial Eyes

Artificial eyes are cared for by qualified staff unless the person's care plan states otherwise. To clean an artificial eye, it must be handled carefully to prevent scratching or breaking.

· Wash your hands before and after touching the eye.

· Clean the eye over a sink or basin half-full of warm water (to avoid breakage if dropped).

· Wet the eye under warm, running water.

· Rub the eye *gently* with clean sterile gauze.

· Rinse the eye under the running water.

Part 4	Caring for Mobility Aids *(U2.b, Z6.b)*

Be sure equipment is in good repair and is used correctly.

Many people use aids for mobility. You are responsible for observing and reporting any problems in using the equipment and any repairs that are needed.

· Provide relevant information on use and care.

· Demonstrate use of the aid if necessary.

· Clear the immediate area of potential hazards.

· Provide the necessary support, feedback, and encouragement for the person to fully and correctly use the appliance.

· Check that the appliance continues to be appropriate and effective for the person's use. If not, ask for advice.

· Label any defective or broken device and take it out of circulation for repair or disposal.

Wheelchairs

When using a wheelchair, be sure the person is properly positioned for comfort and safety. Wheelchairs are equipped with a variety of options:

· removeable arm rests

· heel rests

· special seat cushions

To maintain wheelchairs:

· Check for loose, worn, or missing parts.

· Check the brakes.

· Oil metal parts once a week.

· Keep the chair clean.

· Be sure the chair is properly adjusted for the person.

Canes

Canes are used for balance or to support weight.

· For balance, the cane is carried on the person's strong side.

· For supporting weight, the cane is carried on the weak side.

To check canes:

· Check the tips for worn cups.

· Check canes for cracks or loose screws.

· Be sure that the person is using the cane properly.

Crutches

People who use crutches should be checked regularly for friction sores.

To check crutches:

· Check the crutch tips.

· Check the padding for wear.

· Check for loose screws or cracks.

Zimmer Frames

The type of Zimmer frame that is used depends on the individual's needs and ability. Zimmer frames are ordered by a doctor or physiotherapist.

A standard Zimmer frame is rigid with four legs. It is used for balance.

A gliding Zimmer frame is the same as the standard Zimmer frame except there are wheels on the front legs. It can be pushed without having to pick it up.

A reciprocal walker has a hinged frame and moves forward one side at a time.

To check Zimmer frames:

· Make sure the Zimmer frame is the correct size for the person.

· Check for loose screws.

· Check for worn tips.

Review

1. Describe how to care for sensory and mobility aids.

_____

_____

_____

_____

2. Describe proper maintenance for hearing aids.

_____

_____

_____

3. Identify three or more ways to prevent damage or loss to glasses.

_____

_____

_____

4. How would you encourage the use of mobility aids?

_____

_____

_____

5. What are three or more safety precautions for wheelchairs?

_____

_____

_____

_____

6. What are three observations for checking safe use of canes?

a) *Whether the person is using the cane correctly.*

_____

_____

_____

7. What are safety precautions for checking Zimmer frames?

_____

_____

_____

Module 10

Specific Health Problems

Your patience and support enhance the quality of life for people with health problems.

Objectives:

- ☐ Describe how to care for people who are confused
- ☐ Describe reality orientation
- ☐ Describe methods for dealing with insomnia
- ☐ Identify the symptoms of diabetes
- ☐ Describe the five stages of grief
- ☐ Recognise physical changes of ageing
- ☐ Identify reactions to death and dying
- ☐ Describe care of the body after death

Need-to-Know Words:

- · confusion
- · insomnia
- · diabetes
- · seizures
- · ageing
- · grief
- · post-mortem

| **Part 1** | **Dealing with Confusion** *(X1.c)* |

A confused person feels insecure and frustrated.

Confusion is not a disease; it is a side effect of other problems. Confusion is caused by a decreased blood supply to the brain cells which can result from severe emotional stress, disease, infection, medication, or injury. It is important to chart the first time a person shows confused behaviour; it may be a warning sign of stroke, dehydration, or fever.

The confused person may need to be reminded of daily activities such as eating, bathing, dressing, and toileting. The person may become fearful and frustrated.

Reality orientation is a major part of caring for confused people. Repetition is very important.

- Repeat the person's name often.

- Identify yourself each time you visit the person.

- Always speak slowly and calmly.

- Use simple words that the person understands.

- Put calendars and clocks where they are easily seen.

- Repeat the day, date, and time often.

- Open the drapes during the day and close them at night.

- Discuss familiar people, objects, and events, and keep familiar pictures visible.

- Encourage the person to watch TV and listen to the radio.

- Protect the person from injury; he or she may not be aware of hazards.

- Give instructions that are easy to follow, and repeat as often as necessary.

- Ask a simple question and allow time for a response.

- Never rush the person.

- Maintain a predictable routine and be consistent.

- Avoid rearranging furniture.

- Provide quiet.

- Watch the person closely to prevent wandering.

| **Part 2** | **Dealing with Insomnia** *(Z19.b)* |

Sleep repairs the "wear and tear" of waking hours.

Insomnia is a disorder of initiating and maintaining sleep. Sleep is an important process to remedy "wear and tear" during the waking hours. Before there is any attempt to treat insomnia, a thorough assessment of the causes is essential.

Factors that can affect the ability to sleep:

- illness, coughing, or pain

- worry or thinking

- the sleep environment (e.g., comfort of the bed, temperature, or lighting)

- stimulation (e.g., caffeine)

- the need to use the toilet

- level of tiredness

- interrupted pre-sleep routine

Possible solutions (focusing on causes):

· a sleep-compatible bedtime routine
  (e.g., a hot milky drink and a good novel)

· drinking decaffeinated coffee or tea,
  especially in the evening

· not having naps during the day

· using relaxation techniques

· buying a new bed

As a last resort, a doctor may prescribe medication to help relaxation or induce sleep.

Part 3	**Caring for Diabetes Mellitus** *(U4.e)*

Report any changes or pain.

Diabetes results when the body cannot produce enough insulin. Insulin is a hormone produced by the pancreas to help the body break down and convert sugars and starches into energy.

Symptoms

· thirst

· frequent urination

· fatigue

· skin is easily irritated and slow to heal

· blurred vision

· weight loss

· muscle cramps

General Care

· Monitor the person's intake and report any food not consumed.

· Protect against cuts and scrapes. Diabetics heal slowly and are susceptible to infection; severe infections could result in amputation.

· Report any complaints of pain immediately.

· Report any change in activity or food intake; insulin dosages may need to be adjusted for changes.

· Be sure clothing and bed coverings do not cut off blood circulation.

· Provide good skin care.

· Report any changes in skin colour or temperature.

· Encourage the person to be as self-managing as possible.

Complications

Hyperglycaemia (diabetic coma) is the result of too little insulin or too much sugar. It occurs when blood sugar levels are high and acidosis (inability of the body to excrete toxins) is present. Though the onset is gradual, this is a life-threatening condition requiring immediate care.

Early signs of hyperglycaemia:

· increased urination

· abdominal pain

· nausea

· drowsiness

· thirst

Later signs:

· heavy breathing

· breath smells of pear drops

· flushed face

· dry skin

· loss of consciousness

· death

Treatment:

· Insulin is injected by a qualified nurse.

· Stay with the person and offer support.

· Report any abnormal symptoms immediately.

Hypoglycaemia (insulin shock) is a condition resulting from too much insulin or too little sugar. There is danger of insulin shock when too much insulin has been taken or too little food is consumed. Hypoglycaemia comes on very quickly. Report any attacks of hypoglycaemia immediately to the person-in-charge.

Signs of hypoglycaemia:

· lethargy, weakness, dizziness

· hunger

· sweating

· trembling

· unconsciousness

· death

Treatment:

Glucose (sugar) is given orally. In severe cases, glucose may be injected intravenously (into the vein) by a doctor.

Part 4	**Dealing with Seizures** (U4.e)

Do whatever is necessary to prevent injury during a seizure.

A seizure (fit) results when normal brain cell activity is disrupted. Seizures can happen to anyone.

Seizures may be caused by:

· tumors

· head injury

· fever

· chemical imbalance

· stroke

Sometimes no cause can be found for a person who has seizures. When a person tends to have repeated seizures, even rarely, the person is said to be suffering from epilepsy.

The main treatment for epilepsy is medication. Medication strengthens a person's resistance to seizures. It is important that people who have epilepsy take their medication regularly, as prescribed. Epilepsy may be completely controlled with medication, or at least the number of seizures is kept to a minimum.

People who suffer from epilepsy should be encouraged to follow life-styles that are as full and normal as possible. However, they should not take any unnecessary risks (e.g., working with machinery).

Types of Seizures

Generalised absence (petit mal) seizures are characterised by the person looking blank and staring. There may be slight blinking or twitching. This type of seizure lasts for a few seconds and then normal activity continues.

Generalised tonic-clonic (grand mal) seizures tend to have a common sequence of events: staring, stiffening of the body (falling to the ground), possible blue colour around the mouth, convulsions (jerking movements). As breathing restarts, normal colouring returns. There may be blood-flecked saliva and incontinence (rarely). This type of seizure lasts for a few minutes.

Status epilepticus occurs when a person has repeated tonic-clonic seizures without recovering consciousness. The person may die if not given medical treatment immediately.

Complex partial (psychomotor) seizures may start with an "aura" or waning. The person appears confused or distracted and may repeat a series of movements (e.g., plucking at clothes).

During the Seizure:

1. Call for help.

2. Do whatever is necessary to protect the person from injury.

3. Do not leave the person.

4. Help the person lie down.

5. Place a pillow under the head.

6. If possible, turn the head to one side to prevent choking.

7. Move furniture and equipment out of the way if the seizure occurs on the floor.

8. If the person is in bed, pad the side rails with blankets or soft foam.

Do not try to restrain the person.

Do not pry the mouth open.

Do not insert anything into the mouth.

After the Seizure:

1. Be aware that the person will not remember the seizure.

2. Help the person into bed.

3. Put up the side rails for protection.

4. Offer comfort and support.

5. Report all seizures to the person-in-charge.

6. Chart that the seizure was observed and reported.

7. Observe closely in case the person is confused or has another seizure.

| Part 5 | Physical Changes Related to Ageing (U4.a) |

Help people adapt to the physical changes of ageing.

System	Potential Problems	What To Do
Cardiovascular	· heart muscle loses strength · arteries/veins get narrower, reduce blood flow · less oxygen to entire body · slower healing	Work with the care team to develop an exercise program. Encourage exercise based on the care plan. Report tiring from exercises.
Nervous	· loss of brain cells · less blood to brain · forgets recent events · confusion, dizziness	Do not rush the person. Allow time for decisions. Avoid abrupt schedule changes. Encourage thinking, reading, mental exercises.
Sensory	· reduced vision, hearing · decreased taste, smell · reduced sense of touch, less likely to feel pain · voice muscles lose strength	Encourage use of glasses and hearing aids if needed. Speak slowly and clearly. Listen carefully when the person speaks. Encourage good nutrition even though the food may not taste good to the person.
Respiration	· lungs lose strength · more lung deposits possible · harder to breathe	Get the person out of bed often. Encourage exercise. Use light bed covers. Occasional coughing clears lungs.
Musculo-skeletal	· muscle atrophy, lose strength · bones lose density, get more brittle · joints less flexible · gradual height loss	Avoid falls; hip fractures can be deadly. Position and walk as indicated in the care plan.

System	Potential Problems	What To Do
Skin / Integrity	· skin drys, less elastic · wrinkles, age spots appear · skin loses fatty layer so person gets cooler · surface blood vessels weaken · nails thicken, toughen · hair turns grey, falls out · skin bruises easily	If bedridden, change positions frequently to help prevent pressure sores. Smooth wrinkles from linen. Keep skin clean and dry. Use lotions for moisture. Remove safety hazards. Use extreme care clipping nails. Layer bed covers for warmth.
Digestive	· less saliva production · more difficulty swallowing · loss of teeth, harder to chew · less taste, less appetite · more frequent constipation · more indigestion	Encourage fluids. Allow plenty of time to eat. Make sure dentures are in place if used. Encourage frequent toileting and establish bowel movement regularity.
Urinary	· reduced kidney function · less bladder control, incontinence · more frequent urination	Encourage daytime drinking of fluids. If the person is incontinent, do not criticise. Follow bladder training programme.
Reproductive	· less ability to get, maintain erection in men · menopause in women · reduced vaginal lubrication	Recognise that people of all ages are sexual beings. Allow time and privacy for a person's sex life. Be willing to discuss sex openly. Never tease, criticise, or embarrass a person.
Endocrine	· decreased hormone levels · less body water so weight loss · less ability to handle stress · more likely to become ill · takes longer to get well	Wash hands often and well. Keep surroundings clean to prevent infection. Reduce stress and avoid schedule changes. Offer encouragement, not criticism.

| Part 6 | **Dealing with Dying** *(O.d.e, W2.a.b.c.d, W8.a)* |

Fear is a common reaction to death.

You may have to care for people in the last stages of life. Do not allow your fear of death to stop you from being sensitive to the people's needs. Offer concerned care and understanding.

If you have lost a loved one, think about how you felt. Consider how death was handled by the family, medical staff, and friends. Reflect on what comforted you and what upset you. Use your experiences to provide appropriate care.

- Make the person as comfortable as possible.
- Continue normal care.
- Encourage the person to suggest how he or she prefers to be supported.
- Do not leave the person alone.
- Keep the room well lighted; darkness may be frightening.
- Keep the room well ventilated.
- Talk in a normal voice.
- Do not tiptoe.
- Provide comfort and support for the person and the family.
- Respect the need for time and privacy with close family and friends.
- Provide spiritual support if requested.
- Allow the person to die with dignity.

Stages of Grief

People who believe they are about to die react in different ways. Moods may change from day to day as they grieve over life ending. Family members may experience the same feelings.

In her work with dying patients, Dr. Elizabeth Kubler-Ross identified five stage of grief. The stages apply to any major loss.

- denial
- bargaining
- anger
- acceptance
- depression

Not everyone goes through all five stages, nor is there a specific order. Some may repeat stages. Being familiar with the five stages of grief will help you understand what the person and the family are experiencing.

Denial is a state of shock when the person cannot accept what is happening. The person may insist it is a mistake or may ignore the facts completely.

- Do not force people to face the truth.
- Give people time to adjust.
- Listen when people want to talk.
- Do not force conversation.

Anger is normal. People express anger at God, at the doctor, at life, perhaps even at you. They may yell at you, accuse you of poor care, complain about everything, or refuse to do anything you ask.

- Be patient.
- Continue giving the best care you can.
- Do not take insults personally.
- Do not become defensive.

Depression happens when people have partially accepted death. They are sorting out their feelings. Sometimes people become very withdrawn and may not want to eat or socialise. Others become more talkative and need more of your time.

- Being there for the person is very important. If he or she wants to talk, listen patiently.

- Be compassionate. If the person does not want to talk, do not force conversation.

- Give the best care possible.

Bargaining is when people try to make deals to postpone death. They will bargain with God or the doctors. Sometimes they may try to bargain with you.

- Listen with a caring attitude.

- Never make promises or say, "Things will be all right."

- Let the person know you are there for them.

- Hold the person's hand for comfort.

Acceptance is when the person accepts that death is inevitable. It does not mean that he or she wants to die. The person may be talkative or may be very quiet. Spending time with close relatives or friends may be very comforting for the person.

- Be there to hold a hand and keep the person from feeling alone.

- Continue routine care.

- Provide privacy with loved ones.

- If a clergy member is requested, let the person-in-charge know immediately.

Care of the Body After Death

Post-mortem (after death) care begins as soon as the person is pronounced dead. A trained nurse is usually responsible for laying out the body. You may be asked to assist.

Some religions prohibit the body being laid out by the care staff after death. Laying out the body is done by specific relatives or religious leaders as part of a religious service.

The right to be treated with respect and dignity and the right to privacy apply after death as well as during life.

- Position the body in normal alignment.

- Close the eyes gently.

- Insert dentures if appropriate.

- Close the mouth.

- Cover the body to the shoulders with a sheet if the family is to view the body.

- Give the body a bed bath.

- Brush or comb the hair.

- Shave the face of the male, if necessary.

Review

1. Identify six or more ways to help a person who is suffering from confusion.

   a) Repetition
   _____
   _____
   _____
   _____

2. What are some causes and possible solutions for insomnia?

   _____
   _____
   _____
   _____

3. Identify three types of seizures and the characteristics of each.

   _____
   _____
   _____
   _____

4. Identify symptoms of diabetes.

   _____
   _____
   _____
   _____

5. How would you prevent injury during a seizure?

   _____
   _____
   _____
   _____

6. Discuss physical changes related to ageing.

   _____
   _____
   _____
   _____

7. Describe the five stages of grief.

   _____
   _____
   _____
   _____

Practical Skills

Your training includes hands-on practice.

To gain a Level 2 National or Scottish Vocational Qualification (NVQ/SVQ) in Care, you must be able to demonstrate skills for providing quality care services.

Go through the following list and tick off those skills you feel confident you can perform to the best of your ability. Work on those you leave unticked.

- ☐ Maintains and respects people's rights regardless of race, religion, or life style.
- ☐ Promotes self-care and independence based on a person's capabilities.
- ☐ Recognises a person's right to decisions about personal care.
- ☐ Recognises a person's need for privacy and maintains confidentiality.
- ☐ Reports the concerns of people in care.
- ☐ Demonstrates safety and emergency procedures.
- ☐ Maintains the health and safety of the care environment.
- ☐ Identifies common basic needs.
- ☐ Assists people in getting to and participating in recreation and leisure activities.
- ☐ Uses good communication, counselling, and interpersonal skills.
- ☐ Accurately records and promptly reports pertinent observations, using appropriate terms.
- ☐ Recognises how disease-causing micro-organisms are spread.
- ☐ Demonstrates procedures for infection control (including hand washing).
- ☐ Provides care and security for people's personal possessions.
- ☐ Measures and records vital signs.
- ☐ Measures and records height and weight.
- ☐ Measures and records fluid and food intake and output.
- ☐ Evaluates food and fluid needs.
- ☐ Recognises and reports abnormal signs and symptoms.
- ☐ Uses correct charting procedures.
- ☐ Shows sensitivity to emotional, social, and mental health needs.
- ☐ Promotes the physical comfort of people in care.
- ☐ Demonstrates good judgment in emergencies.

Practical Skills

☐ Demonstrates basic care:

- bed making
- grooming
- skin care
- bathing
- dressing
- lifting, turning, positioning, and transferring
- mouth care
- toileting
- elimination
- nail care
- feeding

☐ Uses good lifting technique for moving or positioning people.

☐ Provides a clean, orderly, and safe environment.

☐ Demonstrates proper use and storage of cleaning and hazardous materials.

☐ Provides adequate ventilation, warmth, light, and quiet.

☐ Demonstrates appropriate care and use of sensory and mobility aids.

☐ Identifies developmental tasks of ageing, and adjusts for physical and mental limitations.

☐ Displays mature response with issues involving sexuality.

☐ Recognises how family and friends can influence a person's behaviour and care.

☐ Provides care and behaviour that maximises health and safety.

☐ Assures that people in care are free from abuse, mistreatment, or neglect; reports instances of abuse or suspected abuse to appropriate staff.

☐ Accepts responsibility for own actions, and recognises the affect of own behaviour on other people's behaviour.

☐ Recognises behaviour related to the grieving process.

☐ Demonstrates appropriate care for a dying person.

☐ Works within the job description.

☐ Demonstrates the ability to work cooperatively with the care team and to follow instructions.

☐ Is supportive of people in care and their significant others.

☐ Promotes equality and deals with discrimination.

☐ Offers choices whenever possible.

☐ Copes with challenging behaviours.

☐ Obtains, maintains, and transmits information appropriately.

Discover how much you have learned.

Read, write, and review information in this book. Then use the practice test to check your knowledge. The practice test has 34 multiple-choice questions and 16 true/false questions.

Multiple choice: Circle the letter on the left side of the correct answer.

Sample Question 1

The MOST important way to prevent germs from spreading is to:

a. wash your hands before and after contact with each person in your care

b. drink plenty of fluids

c. avoid any unnecessary contact with people in your care

d. confine people in your care to their rooms

The correct answer is: "wash your hands before and after contact with each person in your care." Circle the letter "a," next to the correct answer.

True/False: Circle T if the statement is true or F if the statement is false.

Sample Question 2

T F **You are an important member of the care team.**

The statement is true. Circle the letter "T".

Now you are ready to begin the practice test. Read each question carefully before marking the answer. If you are not sure, mark the answer you think is correct.

Multiple Choice

1. **The MOST important members of the care teams are:**
   a. the doctors
   b. the nurses
   c. the people in care
   d. the social workers

2. **Difficult behaviour may be displayed by the people in your care as a result of:**
   a. a need for comfort and understanding
   b. old age
   c. stubbornness
   d. bad manners

3. **If a person is visually impaired, you should:**
   a. scold the person for not wearing glasses
   b. identify yourself whenever you enter the room
   c. discourage the person from being self-managing
   d. avoid talking to the person

4. **The MOST important measure to prevent the spread of infection is:**
   a. fresh air
   b. clean clothing
   c. hand washing
   d. isolation

5. **When lifting, it is correct to:**
   a. bend at the waist
   b. keep your back straight
   c. keep your knees straight
   d. keep your feet close together

6. **The primary concern when moving a person is to:**
   a. hurry
   b. keep the person happy
   c. use the muscles in your back for lifting
   d. provide safety

7. **The pulse measures:**
   a. respiration
   b. blood pressure
   c. activity
   d. heart beats

8. **The average pulse rate per minute for adults is:**
   a. 16 - 23
   b. 25 - 37
   c. 42 - 53
   d. 56 - 80

9. **The radial pulse is located in the:**
   a. neck
   b. wrist
   c. temple
   d. foot

10. **One respiration equals:**
    a. one inspiration and one expiration
    b. two full breaths
    c. two inspirations
    d. one inhalation

11. **If something seems wrong with a person, you would:**
    a. check on the person in an hour
    b. do nothing until you know what the problem is
    c. report it
    d. tell the person's family

12. **If you are unable to work, it is MOST important to:**
    a. inform your manager when you are fit to return
    b. inform your manager at the earliest opportunity that you are unable to work
    c. inform your manager when you expect to be fit to return to work
    d. send a sick note to your manager

13. **It is important for you to:**
    a. encourage the people in your care to be independent
    b. dress and feed the people in your care, even when they are able to dress and feed themselves
    c. discourage the people in your care from talking about their problems
    d. always tell the person's family about his or her problems

14. **If people are able to assist with their personal care, you would:**
    a. provide the care yourself because it is faster and easier
    b. tell them to hurry
    c. let people do it, even if it takes more time and effort than doing it yourself
    d. discourage people from trying

15. **For a person who is having nil-by-mouth, mouth care should be carried out:**
    a. once a day
    b. at least twice a day
    c. every two hours
    d. only as necessary

16. **If there is a foreign body firmly embedded in a wound, you would:**
    a. use direct pressure to control bleeding
    b. use indirect pressure to stop bleeding
    c. tightly bandage the affected area over the foreign body
    d. remove it

17. **Foot care is given only by a chiropodist if a person:**
    a. takes any medications
    b. has poor circulation or is diabetic
    c. wants special treatment
    d. is aggressive

18. **Serving the wrong meal to a person:**
    a. is never a problem
    b. is okay, but be more careful next time
    c. makes more work for yourself
    d. can cause severe problems

19. **Range of movement exercises are important because the exercises:**
    a. give people in care something to do
    b. keep you busy
    c. maintain mobility and prevent atrophy
    d. cause contractures

20. **Help prevent dehydration by:**
    a. cutting back on fluid intake
    b. encouraging fluid intake
    c. bathing twice a day
    d. withholding fluids

21. **The average fluid intake per day is:**
    a. 2000 ml or more
    b. 1800 ml or more
    c. 200 ml
    d. 3 full glasses

22. **The best way to prevent accidents is:**
    a. telling people in your care to be careful
    b. getting angry when a person has an accident
    c. placing the call light out of a person's reach
    d. being alert to safety hazards

23. **The leading cause of injury to older people is:**
    a. falling
    b. burns
    c. accidental poisoning
    d. choking

24. **Disinfectants should be:**
    a. readily available
    b. kept in open cupboards
    c. locked in storage areas
    d. kept in handy locations

25. **The universal sign for choking is:**
    a. coughing
    b. clutching the stomach
    c. clutching the throat
    d. dysphagia

26. **The Heimlich Manoeuvre is used only when:**
    a. there is a complete obstruction of the airway
    b. a person is comatose
    c. a person complains of chest pains
    d. a person asks for help

27. **Before putting a person in the bath:**
    a. ask the person to check the water temperature by hand
    b. check that the water temperature is between 35-36 degrees centigrade, using a bath thermometer
    c. ensure that the towels are warmed
    d. Make sure that there is talcum powder in the person's toilet bag

28. **According to the Patient's Charter, each person has the right:**
    a. to be registered with a General Practitioner
    b. of access to the family's health records
    c. to demand a hospital bed
    d. to demand a home visit

29. **People who are incontinent of urine:**
    a. should be scolded when they have an "accident"
    b. are usually too lazy to go to the bathroom
    c. sometimes regain bladder control with appropriate training
    d. should restrict their fluid intake

30. **Reality orientation is used:**
    a. for people who cannot remember recent events
    b. to help people remember past events
    c. to introduce someone to a new place of residence
    d. to introduce new staff to the organisation

31. **The FIRST thing you should do if a person has a seizure is:**
    a. leave the room to find help
    b. hold the person's hand
    c. restrain the person
    d. protect the person from injury

32. **A pyrexia is a temperature:**
    a. below 37.5 degrees centigrade
    b. below 35 degrees centigrade
    c. above 37.5 degrees centigrade
    d. above 35 degrees centigrade

33. **During the final stages of life you should:**
    a. leave the person alone
    b. continue normal care
    c. discourage visitors
    d. keep the room dark

34. **When on duty, you should report to the:**
    a. doctor
    b. director of personnel
    c. senior social worker
    d. person-in-charge

True/False

35. T F You have a legal and moral responsibility to keep information about the people in your care confidential.

36. T F Good listening skills are important.

37. T F HIV/AIDS cannot be prevented.

38. T F Never wear gloves when handling blood or body fluids.

39. T F Washing your hands is the most important preventive measure for infection control.

40. T F Check the carotid artery in the leg, next to the knee when the pulse is too weak to feel at the wrist.

41. T F Denial is a state of shock when a person cannot accept what is happening.

42. T F Fluid measurements are recorded in millilitres.

43. T F Incontinence is bowel elimination that is infrequent and painful.

44. T F Use good lifting technique to prevent back injuries.

45. T F Ageing skin is fragile and damages easily.

46. T F Your attitude and behaviour do not affect other people's behaviour.

47. T F In case of fire, the first step is to locate a fire extinguisher.

48. T F The first sign that a pressure sore is developing is a break in the skin.

49. T F Any complaints from people in your care should be reported.

50. T F You should allow people in your care to make personal choices whenever possible

Correct Answers

50. T	49. T	48. F	47. F	46. F	45. T	44. T	43. F	42. T	41. T
40. F	39. T	38. F	37. F	36. T	35. T	34. d	33. b	32. c	31. d
30. a	29. c	28. a	27. a	26. a	25. c	24. c	23. a	22. d	21. a
20. b	19. c	18. d	17. b	16. b	15. c	14. c	13. a	12. b	11. c
10. a	9. b	8. d	7. d	6. d	5. b	4. c	3. b	2. a	1. c

Anderson, D. (ed), *A Diet of Reason: Sense and Nonsense in the Healthy Eating Debate*, Social Affairs Unit, London, 1986.

Anderson, Samuel L., M.D., *The New Home Medical Encyclopedia*, Volume 2, Quadrangle Books, 1973.

Back Tips for Health Care Providers, Krames Communications, California, 1986.

Care Sector Consortium, *National Occupational Standards for Care*, HMSO, London, 1992.

Chadwick, D. and S. Usiskin, *Living with Epilepsy*, Macdonald & Co., London, 1987.

Clarke, M., *Practical Nursing*, Balliere Tindall, Eastbourne, 1983.

Consumer Guide, *Family Medical & Health Guide*, Publications Int'l., Lincolnwood, Illinois, 1985.

Daniels, Leola, *Competencies for Nursing Assistants - A Curriculum Guide*, Idaho, 1989.

Department of Employment, *Health and Safety at Work Act*, HMSO, London, 1974.

Department of Health, *Access to Health Records Act*, HMSO, London, 1990.

Department of Health, *Caring for People: Community Care in the Next Decade and Beyond*, HMSO, London, 1989.

Department of Health, *Disabled Persons Act*, HMSO, London, 1986.

Department of Health, *Harassment at Work*, NHSME Advance Letter (GC) 2/92, 1992.

Department of Health, *Health and Healthy Living: A Guide for Older People*, HMSO, London, 1991.

Department of Health, *The Health of the Nation*, HMSO, London, 1992.

Department of Health, *HIV: The Causative Agent of AIDS and Related Conditions*, Second Revision of Guidelines, Advisory Committee on Dangerous Pathogens, HMSO, London, 1990.

Department of Health, *An Introduction to the Children Act 1989*, HMSO, London, 1989.

Department of Health, *Mental Health (Amendment) Act*, HMSO, London, 1982.

Department of Health, *National Health Service and Community Care Act*, HMSO, London, 1990.

Department of Health, *On the State of the Public Health for the Year 1991: Health of Black and Ethnic Minorities*, HMSO, London, 1992.

Department of Health, *The Patient's Charter*, HMSO, London, 1991.

Department of Health, *Working Together under the Children Act 1989*, HMSO, London, 1991.

Department of Trade and Industry, *Data Protection Act*, HMSO, London, 1984.

Food Sense, *The Food Act 1990 and You: A Guide for the Food Industry*, Food Sense, London, 1991.

Gillogly, Barbara, *Skills and Techniques for the New Nursing Assistant*, Medcom, Inc. and Quality Care Health Foundation, California, 1990.

Great Britain Health and Safety Commission, *Manual Handling of Loads: Proposals for Regulations and Guidance, Consultative Document No. 36*, Health and Safety Executive, London, 1991.

Health Education Council, *Mind Your Back*, HEC, London, 1984.

Home Office, *Access to Personal Files Act*, HMSO, London, 1987.

Home Office, *Access to Personal Files (Social Services) Regulations*, HMSO, London, 1989.

Home Office, *Access to Personal Files (Social Services - Amendment) Regulations, LAC(91)11*, HMSO, London, 1991.

Home Office, *Food Safety Act*, HMSO, London, 1990.

Home Office, *Race Relations Act*, HMSO, London, 1976.

Bibliographical Resources

Home Office, *Sex Discrimination Act*, HMSO, London, 1975.

Kubler-Ross, Elizabeth, *On Death and Dying*, Macmillan, New York, 1969.

Lloyd, P. et al, *The Handling of Patients: A Guide for Nurses (2nd edition)*, Back Pain Association, Teddington, 1987.

Lloyd, P.V. et al (eds), *The Handling of Patients: A Guide for Nurses(2nd edition)*, Back Pain Association and Royal College of Nursing, London, 1988.

Mace, Nancy and Peter Rabins, *The 36 Hour Day*, Johns Hopkins University, Maryland, 1988.

Maslow, Abraham, *Toward a Psychology of Being (2nd edition)*, D. Van Nostrand, Princeton, New Jersey, 1962.

McNaught, Allan, *Health Action and Ethnic Minorities*, Bedford Square Press, London, 1987.

Medical Defense Union, *AIDS: Medico-Legal Advice*, Medical Defense Union, London, 1990.

Mullen, Lynn and Janet Fouts, *Nursing Assistant Training Manual*, Oregon Medical Express, Oregon, 1989.

National Extension College, *Caring for Everyone: Ensuring Standards of Care for Black and Ethnic Minority Patients*, NEC, London, 1991.

Nelson-Jones, R., *The Theory and Practice of Counselling Psychology*, Holt, Rinehart and Winston, London, 1984.

Rider, Janis, Elizabeth Nowlis and Patricia Bentz, *Modules for Basic Nursing Skills*, Houghton Mifflin, Massachusetts, 1980.

Schniedman, Rose, Susan Lambert and Barbara Wander, *Being a Nursing Assistant*, 5th Ed., Prentice Hall, New Jersey, 1989.

Sorrentino, Sheila, *Mosby's Textbook for Nursing Assistants*, C.V. Mosby, St. Louis, Missouri, 1987.

United Kingdom Central Council for Nursing, Midwifery and Health Visiting, *Code of Professional Conduct*, UKCC, London, 1984.

United Kingdom Central Council for Nursing, Midwifery and Health Visiting, *Confidentiality*, UKCC, London, 1987.

Wessex Regional Health Authority, *AIDS Response Manual (2nd edition)*, WRHA, Winchester, 1991.

Will, Connie and Judith Eighmy, *Being a Long-Term Care Nursing Assistant (3rd edition)*, Prentice Hall, New Jersey, 1991.

World Health Organisation, *Targets for Health for All: Implications for Nursing/Midwifery*, WHO, Geneva, 1986.

Glossary of Terms

A

abduction — moving body part away from body

abuse — physical, mental, or sexual harm, exploitation or neglect

acidosis — inability of blood to get rid of toxins

adduction — moving body part toward body

ageing — physical and mental process of growing old

AIDS — Acquired Immune Deficiency Syndrome: disease that attacks the immune system, preventing the body from fighting infection

aids (sensory or mobility) — equipment that helps a person regain lost function

alignment — keeping a straight line

ambulate — to walk

aphasia — difficulty using or understanding words

arteries — blood vessels that carry blood from the heart to the system

arteriosclerosis — hardening of the arteries

artificial — a copy or substitute

asepsis — procedures to reduce disease-causing organisms

aspiration — breathing solids or fluids into the lungs

assault — an unlawful personal attack

atrophy — wasting away of muscle or other tissue

attitude — the way a person acts

autoclave — intense heat sterilizing

axillary — in the armpit

B

bacteria — disease-causing germs

barrier — obstacle blocking approach, path, or goal

basic needs — essential physical and emotional requirements

battery — an attack when an actual blow is delivered

bedpan — a pan used for elimination while confined to bed

bedside commode — chair with a bedpan

beliefs — individual viewpoint, opinions, and feelings

brachial pulse — pulse point at the inside elbow

C

cane — walking stick used for balance or to support weight

care team — everyone who provides care for a person, including professionals, relatives, and the person receiving care

carotid pulse — pulse point on each side of the neck

centre of gravity — area where the bulk of an object is centered

charting — writing in a person's health record

combustible — any material that will ignite or burn easily

commode — moveable chair containing a built-in bedpan

communication — exchanging information (talking, writing, gestures, etc.)

confidentiality — not revealing private information about others

confusion — mentally unclear or uncertain

constipation — difficult or painful bowel movement

consume — taking into the body

contaminate — to infect by contact with a non-sterile object

contraction — shortening and thickening of a muscle

CPR — cardiopulmonary resuscitation, first aid procedure for giving respiration and/or heart massage to revive a person

crutch — support that fits under the armpit

D

decubitus ulcer — sore caused by pressure

deep venus thrombosis — blood clots that form in the deep veins of the leg which can break away and cause serious damage to other parts of the body

defaecate — eliminating waste from the bowels

defamation — oral or written words that damage someone's reputation

Glossary of Terms

degenerate	breaking down
dehydration	too little fluid in body tissues
dementia	mental abilities worsen steadily
denial	refusing to believe
dentures	false teeth
depression	low spirits, sadness, dejection
diabetes	disorder of carbohydrate metabolism
disinfection	killing or slowing the growth of most micro-organisms
drawsheet	sheet used to move people in bed
dysphagia	difficulty swallowing

E

elimination	the process of removing wastes from the body
emergency	sudden situation that requires immediate action
enema	injecting fluids into the rectum
epilepsy	chronic disease of the nervous system characterised by seizures
equality	having the same value or worth
erection	in males, when the penis becomes rigid
ethics	a standard of conduct
expiration	breathing out
extremity	a hand or foot

F

faeces	body waste from the bowel
false documentation	knowingly recording incorrect information on a person's record
feedback	repeat message to confirm understanding
feeding tubes	special tubes passed into the stomach as a route for providing nourishment
femoral pulse	pulse point in the groin (where abdomen joins thigh)
fibre	roughage essential for proper elimination
first aid	emergency care that is necessary until medical help arrives
fluid balance	maintaining the right amount of body fluids

G

gesture	body movements that express an idea
glucose	sugar
grand mal seizure	type of seizure resulting in the loss of consciousness
grief	reaction to loss

H

haemorrhage	bleeding
HBV	Hepatitis B Virus
health promotion	to promote healthy lifestyle (diet, exercise, etc.)
hearing aid	device worn in the ear to increase sound
hearing impaired	deafness or loss of hearing
Heimlich Manoeuvre	first-aid procedure for choking
hemiplegia	paralysis on one side of the body
hemiparesis	loss of sensation
HIV	Human Immunodeficiency Virus which causes AIDS
hydraulic lift	equipment used to lift people
hygiene	principles of health and disease prevention
hyperglycaemia	abnormally high level of sugar in the blood
hypoglycaemia	abnormally low level of sugar in the blood
hypothermia	a temperature below 35° Celsius

I

immune	not subject to a particular disease because of the presence of antibodies
impaction	inability to pass faeces
incontinence	inability to control bladder and/or bowel functions
independence	not relying on others, self-managing
infection	invasion of disease-producing micro-organisms
insomnia	inability to commence or maintain sleep
inspiration	breathing in

insulin — hormone produced by the pancreas which breaks down sugars and starches

insulin shock — resulting from too much insulin or too little food

intake/output — measure of fluid taken in and voided

intravenous — going directly into the vein

isolation — separating an infectious person from others

L

lateral — lying on side

lethargy — abnormal drowsiness or lack of energy

lifting — raising, moving

lifting technique — using correct body posture to avoid injury when lifting

M

managing information — safely handling and storing records, maintaining confidentiality

Maslow, Abraham — psychologist whose theory of the hierarchy of human needs helps explain behaviour

micro-organism — disease-producing bacteria seen only with a microscope

mobility — ability to move

monkey pole — bar above bed to help a person move or exercise

moving — to change place or position

N

nasogastric tube — soft plastic tube inserted through nose into stomach for feeding and/or medicating

negligence — failure to provide care that is necessary for a person's well-being

nil-by-mouth — no food or fluids by mouth

non-ambulatory — cannot walk

nonverbal — body language, facial expressions, hand gestures

nutrients — substances necessary to life

O

objective reporting — reporting facts only

observing — paying careful attention

obstruction — blockage

oedema — excess fluid in the tissues

oral — of the mouth

osteoporosis — bones become brittle due to calcium loss

P

paraphrase — repeat statement in your own words

pathogens — harmful germs

pedal pulse — pulse point on top of foot

perineal — rectal and genital areas

personal hygiene — a person's cleanliness and grooming

petit mal — a partial seizure which does not result in loss of consciousness

pneumonia — infection of the lungs

popliteal pulse — pulse point at back of knee

positioning — how a person is placed, a particular position

post-mortem — after death

precautions — measures taken beforehand against possible danger

pressure sores — body sores caused by pressure or chafing; also called decubitus ulcers

prone — lying on stomach

prosthesis — artificial body part

protective barriers — coverings to guard against infection (gloves, masks, gowns, etc.)

psychomotor seizure — temporary loss of judgment and motor control

pyrexia — a temperature above 37.5^0 Celsius

R

radial pulse — pulse point at the wrist

range of movement — normal distance that a joint can move

Glossary of Terms

rapport	a close or sympathetic relationship
reciprocal walker	a hinged frame that moves forward one side at a time
recovery position	specific positioning to prevent choking on tongue or vomit
rehabilitation	restoring a person's physical and/or mental abilities
reporting	giving detailed descriptions of observations
respect and dignity	feelings of positive worth for self and others
respiration	breathing, consisting of one inspiration and one expiration
responsibility	being accountable
rights	standards of justice, law, and morality
rupture	the tearing apart of tissue

S

safety hazards	dangerous conditions, obstacles to security
seizure	disorder with convulsions
self-actualisation	achieving dreams or goals
sensory	pertaining to the senses (seeing, hearing, touching, etc.)
sexuality	characteristics or feelings pertaining to sex
shock	shut down of the cardiovascular system
significant others	everyone who is important to a person
slander	written statement that damages another's reputation
slide board	board used to transfer people when there is no chance of spinal injury
spasm	involuntary muscle contractions
status epileptus	repeated tonic-clonic seizures without regaining consciousness
sterile	absence of all disease-producing micro-organisms
sterilisation	process of killing all micro-organisms
stupor	a state in which the senses are partially or completely dulled

subjective reporting	reporting impressions or feelings
supine	lying on back
support	to carry or bear a specific weight

T

temperature	measurement of body heat
therapeutic	aids good health
transfer	moving from one place to another
transfer belt	a belt worn around the waist of a person to be lifted to provide a grip to aid the lifting process
transmit	to pass from one subject to another

U

urinal	container used by males for urinating

V

vein	blood vessel that carries blood to the heart
verbal	words
visually impaired	blindness or loss of sight
vital signs	temperature, respiration, and pulse
void	urinate

W

wellness	absence of illness
wheelchair	chair mounted on wheels
work role	duties and limits of a person's job

Z

Zimmer frame	tubular frame used as a support for walking

Index

Index